Contemporary Chemical Issues:
Study Guide for Chemistry and Allied Health

Charles E. Carraher, Jr.

Florida Atlantic University

CENGAGE
Learning·

Australia • Brazil • Japan • Korea • Mexico • Singapore • Spain • United Kingdom • United States

For product information and technology assistance, contact us at
Cengage Learning Customer & Sales Support, 1-800-354-9706

For permission to use material from this text or product,
submit all requests online at **cengage.com/permissions**
Further permissions questions can be emailed to
permissionrequest@cengage.com

Senior Project Development Manager:
Linda deStefano

Marketing Specialist:
Courtney Sheldon

Senior Production/Manufacturing Manager:
Donna M. Brown

Production Editorial Manager:
Kim Fry

Sr. Rights Acquisition Account Manager:
Todd Osborne

Compilation © 2012 Cengage Learning
ISBN-13: 978-1-285-38622-5

ISBN-10: 1-285-38622-1

Cengage Learning
5191 Natorp Boulevard
Mason, Ohio 45040
USA

Cengage Learning is a leading provider of customized learning solutions with office locations around the globe, including Singapore, the United Kingdom, Australia, Mexico, Brazil, and Japan. Locate your local office at:
international.cengage.com/region.

Cengage Learning products are represented in Canada by Nelson Education, Ltd.

For your lifelong learning solutions, visit **custom.cengage.com.**

Visit our corporate website at **cengage.com.**

Contents

Introductory Science & Chemistry and Allied Health-Study Guide

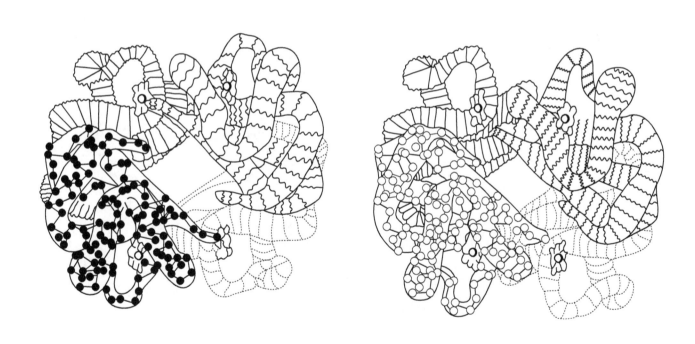

Charles E. Carraher, Jr.

Florida Atlantic University
Boca Raton, FL 33431

Studying Science

Studying science is similar to studying any subject. Following are some ideas that may assist you as you study.

Much of science is abstract. Here we will concentrate on studying chemistry for examples. While much of the study of chemistry is abstract, it is easier to conceptualize by making mind pictures. One topic you will be studying are polymers so we will use polymers to illustrate studying chemistry. Think of what a polymer is and how it should behave. For linear polymers, think of a string or rope. Long ropes get entangled with themselves and other ropes. In the same way, polymer chains entangle with themselves and with chains of other polymers that are brought into contact with them. **Thus, create mental pictures of the polymer molecules as you study them.**

Chemicals and chemistry is real and all about us. We can look at molecules on a micro or atomic level or on a macroscopic level. The PET bottles we have may be composed of long chains of poly(ethylene terephthalate), PET, chains. The aramid tire cord is composed of aromatic polyamide chains. Our hair is made up of complex bundles of fibrous proteins, again polyamides. **The chemistry you study is related to the real world in which we live. We experience "chemistry" at the macroscopic level everyday of our lives and this is a direct consequence of the atomic-level structure and behavior.** Make pictures in your mind that allow you to relate the atomic and macroscopic worlds.

At the introductory level we often examine only the primary factors that may cause particular behavior. Other factors may become important under particular conditions. **The molecules you study at times examine only the primary factors that impact polymer behavior and structure. Even so, these primary factors form the basis for both complex and simple structure-property behavior.**

The structure-property relationships you will be studying are based on well known basic chemistry and physical relationships. **Such relationships build upon one another and as such you need to study in an ongoing manner. Understand as you go along. Read the material BEFORE you go to class.**

This course is an introductory-level course. Each chapter or topic emphasizes knowledge about one or more area. **Science has its own language. It is a language that requires you to understand and memorize certain key concepts.** Our memory can be short term or long term. Short term memory may be considered as that used by an actor or actress for a TV drama. It really does not need to be totally understood, nor retained after the final "take". **Long term memory is required in studying chemistry since it will be used repeatedly and is used to understand other concepts (that is, it is built upon).**

In memorizing, learn how you do this best-time of day, setting, etc. Use as many senses as necessary- **be active**-read your assignment, write out what is needed to be known, say it, listen to yourself say it. Also, look for patterns, create mnemonic devices, avoid cramming too much into too small a time, practice associations in all directions, and test yourself. **Memorization is hard work.**

While knowledge involves recalling memorized material, to really "know" something involves more than simple recall-it involves **comprehension**, **application**, **evaluation**, and **integration** of the **knowledge**. Comprehension is the interpretation of this knowledge, making predictions based on the knowledge, and applying the knowledge to different situations. Analysis involves evaluation of the information and comparing it with other information and synthesis has to do with integration of the information with other information.

In studying chemistry please consider doing the following—

- **skim the text BEFORE the lecture**
- **attend the lecture and take notes**
- **organize your notes and relate information**
- **read and study the assigned material**
- **study your notes and the assigned material and then**
- **review and self-test.**

Learning takes time and effort. Study daily skimming the text and other study material, think about it, visualize key points and concepts, write down important material, make outlines, take notes, study sample problems, etc. All of these help-but some may help you more than others-so focus on these modes of learning-but not at the exclusion of the other aspects.

In preparing for an exam consider the following—

- **accomplish the above-DO NOT wait until the day before the exam to begin studying; create good study habits**
- **study wisely- study how YOU study best-time of day, surroundings, etc.**
- **take care of yourself; get plenty of sleep the night before the exam**
- **attend to last-minute details-is your calculator working, is it the right kind, do I have the needed pencils, review the material once again, etc.**
- **know what kind of test it will be-if possible and**
- **get copies of old exams; talk to others that might have already had the course.**

During the test

- **stay cool, do NOT PANIC;**
- **read the directions; try to understand what is being asked for**
- **in an essay or similar exam work for partial credit; plan your answers**
- **in a multiple choice or T/F exam, eliminate obviously wrong choices**
- **look over the entire exam; work questions that you are sure of; then go to less sure questions; check answers if time permits.**

The study of chemistry contains several types of content-

- **facts**-the term *polymer* means "many" (poly) "units" (mers).
- **concepts**-linear polymers are long molecules like a string
- **rules / relationships / equations**- density is mass per unit volume
- **problems**-what is the density of a material if 10 grams of it occupies 5 milliliters?

These varied types of content are often integrated within any topic, but in this introduction to chemistry, the emphasis is often on concepts but all the aspects are important.

Following are materials intended to assist students taking introductory science and chemistry-intense courses as well as introductory allied health courses. The material is divided according to sections contained in many of these introductory textbooks and is not intended as a substitute for these textbooks but rather is intended to add helps as well as material that assists placement of the topics into perspective.

Science and Chemistry

INTRODUCTION

Science is the study of what is about us which we can measure in some manner. **Chemistry** is a study of matter and the changes it undergoes often on a molecular level. **Chemistry** is a central science important in most of the major issues today and integral in our everyday lives. Begin being more than passive in looking at your lives and the issues of today seeing how chemistry is important in understanding and making informed decisions.

Chemistry is often divided as to being basic or applied. This division is often artificial. Even so, **basic** research, often referred to as fundamental research, looks at fundamental, basic knowledge that underlays all of science. Basic research can lead to useful applications. **Applied** research is the application of basic/fundamental research results that affect our everyday lives in the pills we take, automobiles we drive, water we drink, food we eat, cloths we wear, etc.

Chemicals are all about us. Chemicals are the very basis of both plant and animal life as proteins, nucleic acids, and polysaccharides. In construction they are the concrete, insulation, and wooden and composite beams. At home the materials for our rugs, curtains, coatings, waste paper baskets, water pipes, window glass, ice cube trays, and pillows are chemicals. In transportation they form our air craft, automobiles, ships, and trucks. In communication they form our telephones, TVs, computers, CDs, newspaper, optical fibers, and cell phones. Our foods are chemicals- as meats, vegetables, breads, and cookies. In history chemicals formed the Magna Carter, Torah, Bible, Koran, and our Declaration of Independence. Outside our homes they are present in our flowers, trees, soil, spider webs, and beaches. In fact, it is improbable that a chemical material is not involved in your present activity- reading a paper book, holding a plastic-intense writing device, sitting on a cloth-covered chair or bed, and if your eyes need corrective vision, glasses of one variety or another. The air we breathe is composed of chemicals such as nitrogen, oxygen, carbon dioxide, helium, hydrogen, etc. In fact, if you can touch it, it is composed of chemicals.

You can begin to see that essentially all that we are and come into contact with in our live are chemicals and involve chemistry. Look at the ingredients in the things you buy and see what these ingredients contribute to the product. Begin looking at labels on you foods and medicines. You can get most of the information you need to do this from the web.

SCIENTIFIC METHOD

The **Scientific Method** involves observations, questioning, hypotheses, predictions and tests. All of these involve gathering information and interpreting it with some logic and knowledge. It is something we use daily. We really employ the scientific method in much we do such as when we cook. We see which ingredients and how much give us the particular food and taste we want. Thus, in cooking chocolate chip cookies we might experiment with the ingredients, mixing, and cooking conditions and time. How much butter should we use and what kind. Which chocolate chips and how many should we use. We observe that a particular butter is good giving us the desired fluffy cookies without burning the bottoms of the cookies and without leaving burnt cookie parts on the bottom of the pan. We then experiment, test, it to see if our observation about the use of butter in our cookies to prevent cookies sticking to the bottom of our cooking pans holds. We use different cookie pans to see if our observation is more general and applies to lots of cookie pans. During this time we are making observations, questioning, making predictions (that the butter will give us soft cookies without burning the bottom of the pan), and gather information, all important in the scientific method.

Our observations lead us to create the **hypothesis** that the use of butter in our cookies will self lubricate the cookie sheets, regardless of which cookie sheet we use. We have retested this hypothesis a number of times until we feel confident that our hypothesis is accurate. We ask others to test our hypothesis that adding butter to their chocolate chip cookie dough will provide the necessary lubricant to prevent the cookies from adhering to the bottom of the cookie pan. Their results are consistent with our hypothesis. At this point we might be sufficiently confident to declare that our hypothesis can now be called a theory- the theory of self-lubricating chocolate chip cookie batter.

A **theory** is an idea derived from observations that has "stood the test of time." It has been tested many times with the results consistent with the theory. The theory is a tested explanation for our observations, here with the cookie batter.

We can continue to test our theory eventually gathering sufficient data to call it a "law." **Laws** are really basic descriptions often in mathematical form or a statement about a relationship and while our theory about the lubricating batter may be important, it will probably never reach the importance to be called a law.

In science, we often make measurements to gather data. We want reproducible results. We want results that are accurate and precise. **Accuracy** is agreement with the "correct" value while **precision** is agreement of several measurements with each other.

Qualitative observations are "general" not involving measurements or numbers. The grass is green, Sulfur smells like rotten eggs. **Quantitative observations** involve precise measurements. The reaction of hydrogen and oxygen gives off 40 joules; The crystal weights 3.45 g.

UNITS OF MEASURE

Essentially all of the nations of the world have adopted the metric system to describe measurements. The USA is the lone major nation not to adopt the metric system. The metric system is referred to as the Systeme International d'Unites or SI system for short. It was developed in France in the 18th century and adopted by most of the countries of the world in the 1960s. The metric system is known as a decimalized system where conversion is easily made using a series of prefixes in multiples of ten employed to derive larger and smaller units. Table 1.1 contains some of the most common prefixes. Today, we live in a metric world with talk of the nano world. As we see "nano" is one of the prefixes used to convert to smaller units. The size of the atoms is several nanometers in diameter. So as we today are dealing with atoms and molecules whose dimensions are in the nanometer range we call this the nano world, or attach the prefix nano to whatever we are referring to that has similar dimensions.

Table 1.1 *Important prefixs in the SI system.*

Prefix	Decimal Equivalent	Exponential Equivalent
Kilo	1000.	10^3
No prefix, base unit	1.	10^1
Deci	0.1	10^{-1}
Centi	0.01	10^{-2}
Milli	0.001	10^{-3}
Micro	0.000001	10^{-6}
Nano	0.000000001	10^{-9}
Pico	0.000000000001	10^{-12}

Base physical quantities that you need to be aware of include
length (meter (m)), time, **mass** (gram (g)), **volume** (liter (L), energy, and temperature.

For length, mass, volume, and energy we often use prefixes to denote magnitude. You should know the following prefixes and what they mean.

kilo (kg) means 1,000 or 10^3 (thus a kilogram is 1000 grams)
centa (c) means on hundredth, 0.01 or 10^{-2} (might remember that there are 100 cents in a dollar so a centadollar is one cent)
milli (m) means one thousandth, 0.001 or 10^{-3} and
nano (n) means 0.000000001 or 10^{-9} (a help for remembering the "9" is that nano and nine both begin with the letter "n")

A milliliter or mL is one thousandth (10^{-3}) of a liter and 1 kilometer is one thousand (10^3) meters. Interestingly, one mL = one cubic centimeter or cc = one cubic centimeter cm^3.

MATHEMATICAL SKILLS

Students often say that the mathematics in science is too difficult. The truth is, for elementary courses the mathematics is composed of skills that students have already been exposed to but may need a little reminder of some of the important aspects. Also, it is typically not the mathematical skills that bother students but rather it is to know when to exercise these skills. This study will address both concerns. In this section we will focus on the most common mathematical skills generally needed and will begin to present applications of these skills. Please remember that most of the course focuses on the obtaining of a new language and facts associated with the world about them and that the precise mathematical skills are only a portion of this.

SCIENTIFIC NOTATION

Because we can deal with very large and very small values in science we have developed a way to express these very large and very small values simply. This approach can also be used for everyday values.

A number expressed or written in scientific notation is simply the number written so that it contains one number followed by a period followed by the other numbers and this is multiplied by an appropriate power of ten. It is really simple. Thus, let us say we have 132 marbles. This is expressed in scientific notation as 1.32×10^2. If we have bacteria that is 0.023 mm then in scientific notation it is written as 2.3×10^{-2}.

We see that we can create the power of ten for values greater than 1 by simply counting the number of units we need to move over so that there is only one number to the left of the period. The number of times we move over is equal to the power of ten. Thus, there are about 683,000 people in South Dakota. If we know this to the thousand of people then the scientific notation is written as

$$6\ 8\ 3\ ,\ 0\ 0\ 0 = 6.83 \times 10^5$$

since we moved the "tens" marker or arrow to the left five places the power of ten is 5.

For values less than 1 we do a similar thing except we move the tens marker or arrow to the right. Thus, if the length of a particular hair on our head is 0.0000023 meters this is expressed in scientific notation as

$$0.0\ 0\ 0\ 0\ 0\ 2\ 3 = 2.3 \times 10^{-6}$$

Often we will simply give the number as a simple number such as there were 43 people at our party. While this can be expressed in scientific notation as 4.3×10^1 it would generally be simply given as 43 people.

Watch for this in exam and homework problems. You can generally tell if the number is to be expressed in scientific notation either by them telling you that they want the answer expressed in scientific notation or by what the possible answers. Thus, if they ask us what is 12×11 and the answers are a. 1.2×10^3; b. 1.32×10^2; c. 1.1×10^{-2}; d. 1.12×10^4 we know that they want the answer in scientific notation.

Again, a number written in scientific notation simply means that the value is written with one number to the left of the "." and the number is written to the appropriate power of ten. Here are some additional examples.

3400 becomes 3.4×10^3 55 becomes 5.5×10^1

0.0031 becomes 3.1×10^{-3} 0.000067 becomes 6.7×10^{-5}

560000000 becomes 5.6×10^8 0.0054 becomes 5.4×10^{-3}

PROPORTIONS

Many problems can be solved employing a simple proportion approach. Mathematically if we have

$$\frac{A}{C} = \frac{B}{D}$$

then we can do what is called cross multiplication and set the two equal to one another. Thus AD = BC   From this all the letters can be solved by simply dividing both sides by the appropriate letter. Thus, if we want to solve for A we would divide both sides by D since division of both sides of an equivalency does not change the equivalency. Division of AD = BC by D gives A = CB/D. We can do the same to solve for D giving D = CB/A and for B to give B = AD/C and for C to give C = AD/B. Thus, if we are given three of the values we can determine, solve for, the fourth value.

A similar situation exists where we are given that A = B/C. We can solve for any letter by considering that this can be rewritten as

$$\frac{A}{1} = \frac{B}{C}$$

since we can divide anything by "1" and not change the equation. We can then again cross multiple giving B = AC. Division of both sides by A gives A = B/C allowing us to solve for any of the letters given values for two of the letters. We will employ this particular form of the proportional equation approach when we deal with density.

This approach can utilized for many simple word problems. Thus, if one apple costs 50 cents ($0.50), how much would 24 apples cost. We can reword the problem as a proportion problem so that if one apple costs $0.50, 24 apples would cost how much. Mathematically this is shown as

$$\frac{\text{One apple}}{24 \text{ apples}} = \frac{\$0.50}{X \text{ dollars}}$$

We than solve for X by cross multiplication as follows

one apple × X dollars = $0.50 × 24 apples

Division of both sides of the equation by "one apple" leaves X alone on one side of the equation and allows us to complete the solution for X.

$$\frac{\text{one apple} \times X \text{ dollars}}{\text{one apple}} = \frac{\$0.50 \times 24 \text{ apples}}{\text{one apple}}$$

leaving X cents = $0.50 × 24 apples/one apple = 12 dollars or $12.

Proportions are useful when we know all but one of the values. We will find that one mole of a material has about 6×10^{23} units and that one mole of material weights one gram formula weight. Thus we can calculate the weight of one atom of unit of a material. Thus, one mole of helium, He, weights 4 grams, its formula weight. The weight of one atom of helium is very small and can be stated in words as 6×10^{23} atoms of helium weight 4 grams, 1 atom of helium weights how many grams. In equation form this is

$$\frac{6 \times 10^{23} \text{ atoms of helium}}{1 \text{ atom of helium}} = \frac{4 \text{ grams}}{X \text{ grams}}$$

Solving for X we have X = 4 grams × 1 atom/6×10^{23} atoms = 0.67 × 10^{-23} grams, or as we expected one molecule of helium weighs very little.

We will employ this proportion method to allow us to solve many problems.

MULTIPLICATION AND DIVISION OF POWERS OF TEN

General $\qquad$ $1/10^b = 10^{-b} \ldots$

$1/10^4 = 10^{-4} \ldots$ or $1/10{,}000 = 1/10^4 = 10^{-4} = 0.0001$

General $\qquad$ $1/10^{-b} = 10^b \ldots$

$1/10^{-3} = 10^3 \ldots$ or $1/0.001 = 1/10^{-3} = 10^3 = 1{,}000$

General- Multiplication of Powers of Ten $A \times 10^a \times B \times 10^b = A \times B \times 10^{a+b}$

$3 \times 10^6 \times 2 \times 10^4 = 6 \times 10^{10} \ldots$

$6 \times 10^{-4} \times 1.2 \times 10^{12} = 7.2 \times 10^8 \ldots$

General- Division of Powers of Ten $A \times 10^a / B \times 10^b = (A/B) \times 10^{a-b} \ldots$

$8 \times 10^6 / 2 \times 10^2 = 4 \times 10^4 \ldots$

$6 \times 10^5 / 3 \times 10^{-3} = 2 \times 10^8 \ldots$

$5 \times 10^{-3} / 2 \times 10^{-8} = 2.5 \times 10^5 \ldots$

Complex example $(8 \times 10^6 \times 6 \times 10^{-15})/1.5 \times 10^{-7} = 32 \times 10^{-2} = 3.2 \times 10^{-1}$

Elements of Chemistry

MATTER AND PHASES

Science has its limits; it deals with only events that can be tested and repeated. It deals with things that have physical quantities-mass and energy.

While they are different, we will often use mass (caused by weight of atoms) and weight (gravitational force) interchangeably. Matter occupies space and can be perceived by us.

Matter can be divided according to being solid, liquid or gas. Solids, liquids and gases are called states of matter or **phases**. The three major states of matter or phases are

Solids have a fixed or definite volume and shape. They are rigid and generally have the highest density of the three main phases.

Liquids have a definite volume and occupy the shape of the container but do not always fill the container. Liquids are relatively incompressible.

Gases occupy the entire volume of the container with no fixed shape and they are easily compressed. Gas molecules are relatively far apart.

Matter changes phase with temperature and pressure. Here we will look at only temperature influences (Figure 2.1). Let's start with a cube of ice. It is cold, sufficiently cold so the individual water molecules are locked in place with little movement. As we raise the temperature, we reach a temperature where there is sufficient energy available as heat energy to allow the water molecules to break away from the solid lattice and begin wholesale movement. This point is called the **melting point** and the process is called **melting**. As we increase the temperature we continually add heat energy to the melted ice cube until we have sufficient energy present that allows the liquid water molecules to be ripped from the liquid phase into the gaseous phase. This temperature is called the **boiling point** and the phase change is called **evaporation**.

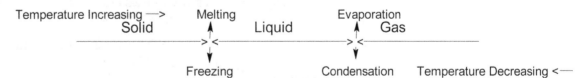

Figure 2.1 *Phases and phase changes as a function of temperature.*

Conversely, we can reduce the thermal energy of vapor water molecules so that they **condense** becoming liquid and as the thermal energy, temperature, is further reduced the liquid water molecules become frozen (**freezing**).

To melt our ice cube takes energy and the same amount of energy is released, given back, when the liquid water returns to the solid, frozen state. Like-wise, the energy required to heat liquid water to become vapor or gaseous water is the same amount of energy released, given back, when the same amount of vapor condenses giving liquid water.

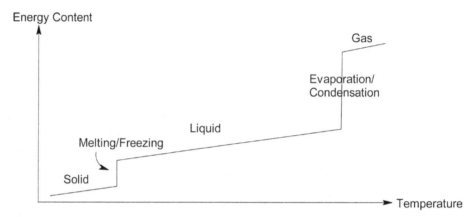

Figure 2.2 *Energy content of wate as a function of temperature.*

DALTON'S ATOMIC THEORY

Till the 1800s there were few unifying basic principles in science and in chemistry. John Dalton put together a listing of some basic principles in 1803 as they knew them. These principles are known as **Dalton's Atomic Theory**. While they are not exactly correct they serve as a good "jumping off" point for our study of the atom.

1. ALL matter is composed of indivisible atoms. Atoms retain their identity in chemical reactions.

$$2H_2 + O_2 \rightarrow 2H_2O$$

2. Atoms are not created, destroyed, or changed into other elements in chemical reactions. So alchemy is out except in nuclear reactions.

3. An element has only ONE kind of atom. Each atom of a given kind has the same properties. These properties are different from the precise properties of atoms of other elements.

4. A compound is composed of atoms of more than one element chemically combined in fixed proportions. A CHEMICAL REACTION consists of an rearrangement of the atoms present in the reacting substance(s) to give a NEW chemical combination. Thus, water contains one oxygen atom and two hydrogen atoms.

5. Atoms of different elements have different masses.

DENSITY

As a material changes phases it also changes the amount of mass within a given volume. Thus, for most materials the density of solids is greater than the same material in a liquid form which is much greater than the density of the material (under room conditions) as a gas. Further, different elements and compounds have different densities.

Archimedes, an ancient Greek philosopher, engineer, and mathematician, in about 250 BC was given the job by King Hiero to determine if a new crown in the shape of a laurel wreath was made out of gold or some other material. He had to do this without damaging the crown. Less expensive silver and other materials were added by dishonest goldsmiths. The density of silver (10.5 g/mL) is about one half that of gold (19.3 g/mL) so the density of a solid gold wreath would be greater than that of a gold-silver mixture. Archimedes was taking a bath at the public bath works and noticed that the level increased as he entered the pool. It dawned on him that he had found how to answer the king's request. It is said that he took off from the pool running in the streets naked yelling "Eureka" which is roughly translated as "I found it." What he found was not how to determine density but rather how to determine the volume of irregularly shaped objects such as the ornate crown. In the following problems you will be given two of the three values needed to determine density, volume, or weight.

Density is the mass/volume. You need to know how to work this relationship. $D = M/V$ Through cross multiplication you get $M = DV$ and though division of both sides by D you get $V = M/D$. Look at the units.

Know density = mass/volume
and how to determine any one of the three-mass, volume or density given the other two. $D = M/V$; $M = DV$; & $V = M/D$

> **Q.** What is the volume of 50 grams of a material with a density of 2g/ml
>
> **A.** $V = M/D = 50\,g/2g/ml = 25\,ml$
>
> **Q.** What is the density of a material that weighs 30 grams and occupies a volume of 10 ml?
>
> **A.** $D = M/V = 30\,g/10\,ml = 3\,g/ml$
>
> **Q.** What is the weight of 40 ml of a material with a density of 4 g/ml?
>
> **A.** $M = DV = 4\,g/ml \times 40\,ml = 160\,g$

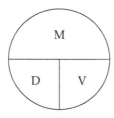

The circle above is an easy way to remember the relationships between mass, density, and volume. Place your finger over the desired quantity and the relationship between the other two is given. Thus, place your finger over "D" and you have M/V so density is mass divided by volume; place your finger over "M" and you have DV so that mass is density times volume.

Elements and Compounds

PHYSICAL AND CHEMICAL PROPERTIES AND CHANGES

We often talk about changes that occur to matter. **Physical changes** involve changes in the form of matter but not in the identity of the matter. It does not involve rearrangement of bonds or atoms. Thus, melting and boiling are physical changes. **Physical properties** also do not involve bond or atom rearrangement. Thus, color, density, solubility, and melting point are all physical properties. When talking about physical properties we can also talk about extensive properties and intensive properties. An extensive property depends on the amount of material present-such as weight and volume of a material. Intensive properties are independent of the amount of material present and include density, melting point and color.

Chemical changes occur when matter is transformed into a new kind of matter or several new kinds of matter through rearrangement of atoms and their bonding. Examples are the rusting of iron and the burning of a candle forming carbon dioxide and water.

A **chemical property** is the tendency by a compound or group of compounds to undergo changes in their chemical structures and involves changes in the arrangement of atoms. Thus, when hydrocarbons, such as petrochemicals like gasoline, are burnt (combusted) they form carbon dioxide and water. When sodium metal comes into contact with water it eventually forms sodium hydroxide.

We typically divide energy into two types-**kinetic energy** which is energy of motion and **potential energy** which is stored or available energy. Oxygen and hydrogen react giving water and lots of energy. Before they react, oxygen and hydrogen have chemical potential energy which is transformed into kinetic energy in the form of heat or an explosion as the reaction occurs.

Atoms and molecules are in some constant motion moving a little depending on the state-like gases are moving a lot whereas atoms and molecules in the solid move very little. This energy of movement is kinetic energy. As heat is applied these atoms/molecules move faster increasing their kinetic energy. As heat is applied the temperature increases.

We have three scales to measure temperature-the centigrade now known as the Celsius scale, Kelvin or Absolute temperature scale, and the one we mostly us in our everyday life, the Fahrenheit scale. Heat flows from a hot object to a cooler object. Think about holding onto an ice cube.

A **chemical reaction**, associated with chemical properties, is the rearrangement of associated atoms. Thus, for the reaction between oxygen and hydrogen to form water we have

$$H_2 + O_2 \rightarrow HOH \text{ (generally written as } H_2O)$$

so that in hydrogen, H_2, each hydrogen atom is associated with another hydrogen atom whereas in water it is associated with oxygen. This formation of water is called a **chemical reaction** and **chemical change**.

Elements are substances that cannot be decomposed by any chemical reaction into simpler substances- Ag, Au, C, Ca, Ba, Fe, O_2, N_2, F_2, Cl_2, Br_2, I_2.

We use a chemical shorthand to describe elements, such as H for hydrogen, O for oxygen, C for carbon. You will need to memorize the first 36 symbols and names along with Sr, Ag, Sn, Sb, I, Ba, Pt, Au, Hg, Pb, Bi, U. We will use a subscript to represent more than one atom. Thus, O_2 means that there are two oxygen atoms; H_2O means there are two hydrogen atoms and one oxygen atom. In fact, a number of elements are **diatomic** in the natural state. The ones you need to know are O_2, N_2, H_2 and all of the halogens such as F_2, Cl_2, Br_2, and I_2.

Compounds are formed when atoms of different elements chemically bond together. Thus H_2O is a compound since it has more than one element in it. Compounds are described using a chemical formula such as H_2O for water and NaCl for sodium chloride, common table salt. For ionic compounds such as NaCl the formula represents the ratio of each type of atom in it. Thus, for NaCl there is one Na and one Cl. For TiO_2 there is one titanium atom for every two oxygen atoms. For covalently bonded compounds the numbers represent the number of each kind of atom within the molecule, a distinct array of only those atoms in the molecule. Thus, benzene is C_6H_6, i.e. a molecule of benzene contains six carbon atoms and six hydrogen atoms.

PERIODIC TABLE

The periodic table is a wonderful guide that allows us to express a lot of chemistry. There are two general types of bonding present in compounds. Bonding can occur through the loss and gain of electrons forming ionic compounds. In general, elements that are towards the left of the periodic table are called **metals** and they often give up electrons when they form compounds forming **ionic compounds** taking on a positive charge becoming **cations**, such as Na^{+1}, Ca^{+2} and Al^{+3}, because they are positively charged. Elements to the left of the periodic table have a greater tendency to pull electrons from the metals, the elements on the right of the periodic table, and are given the name **non-metals**. They take on electrons when they form ionic compounds becoming negatively charged and are given the name **anions**, such as Cl^{-1}, O^{-2} and N^{-3}, because of this negative charge. Many of the non-metals form compounds through sharing electrons forming covalent bonds. Notice that bonding involves electrons and later we will learn that the loss/gain and sharing involves electrons that are furthest from the central positive core or nucleus of atoms.

Metals are the most abundant type of element. As noted above, they are found to the left side of the period table and are separated from the non-metals by an imaginary zig-zag running from Boron to At. Metals often have a "metallic luster" or shine, good conductivity of electricity and heat and are solids (not mercury) at room conditions. Most metals are somewhat malleable (can be hammered into sheets) and ductile (drawn into wires). **Non-metals** are found on the right side of the periodic tale. Solid non-metals are hard and brittle and they are not good conductors. Most form chemical bonds through taking (from metals; forming anions) or sharing electrons (reactions with other non-metals).

Elements along the imaginary zig-zag are referred to as semimetals or **metalloids**. These elements exhibit both metallic and non-metallic properties.

The elements are arranged according to periods and families. **Periods** is the name given to each horizontal row like Na, Mg, Al, Si, P, S, Cl are all in the 3rd period.

The elements are also divided into vertical rows or columns which are called **families** or **groups**. **Members of the same group have similar chemical properties**.

For now let us concentrate on what is referred to as the main group elements. These appear in groups 1 and 2 and 13-18. We will find that these elements have as their valance or outer or bonding electrons "s" and "p" electrons. The first main group column or family or group containing elements such as lithium (Li), sodium (Na) and potassium (K) (but not hydrogen) are called **alkaline metals** and when forming compounds they take on a positive one charge because they give up one negatively charged electron leaving the resulting atom deficient in one electron and it is said to be a plus one charge.

$$\text{Thus, for } Na \rightarrow Na^{+1} + e^{-1} \text{ or } Na \rightarrow Na^{+} + e^{-}$$

The second column or family or group containing elements such as calcium (Ca) and barium (Ba) have the family name of **alkaline earths**. These metals generally give up two electrons when they form compounds so are said to become positively two charged.

$$\text{Thus, for } Ca \rightarrow Ca^{+2} + 2e^{-}$$

The third vertical column containing compounds such as aluminum (Al) and gallium (Ga) generally give up or lose three electrons when they form ionic compounds.

$$\text{Thus, for } Al \rightarrow Al^{+3} + 3\ e^{-}$$

The next main group column of elements containing carbon (C) and silicon (Si) generally do not exchange electrons but rather form covalent bonds.

The next column of elements containing elements such as phosphorus (P) and arsenic (As) generally gain three electrons when they form ionic bonds.

$$P + 3e^{-} \rightarrow P^{-3}$$

The next main group column containing oxygen (O) and sulfur (S) generally gain two electrons when they form ionic compounds.

$$O + 2e^{-} \rightarrow O^{-2}$$

The next main group column that contains fluorine (F) and bromine (Br) is given the name **halogens** and when compounds are derived from them, the halogen atoms are often given the name **halides**. These atoms generally take on a single electron when they form ionic compounds.

$$F + e^- \rightarrow F^-$$

Finally, the last column that contains helium (He) and argon (Ar) have a great tendency to not react, neither sharing nor exchanging electrons. They are known by several names including **rare gases** and **noble gases**.

We will find that the groups or families are arranged so that elements in the same family have the same number of valence or outer electrons in their outer set of orbitals. These valence electrons are the ones involved in forming chemical bonds. We will find that the group 1(also called 1A) or alkaline metals have 1 outer electron which they give up when forming ionic compounds giving cations with a positive one charge; the group 2 (also called 2A) elements have 2 outer electrons which they give up becoming cations with a plus two charge when they form ionic compounds; group 13 (also called 3A) has 3 outer electrons, group 13 (also called 4A) has 4 outer or valence or bonding electrons; etc.

We will discuss more of the periodic table later. Even so, as noted above members of the same family or vertical row tend to have the same valence number meaning they have the same number of bonding electrons and tend to add or lose the same number of electrons. This is shown below for main group elements.

Electrons Lost/Gained	+1	+2	+3	0	−3	−2	−1	0
	H							He
	Li	Be	B	C	N	O	F	Ne
	Na	Mg	Al	Si	P	S	Cl	Ar
	K	Ca	Ga	Ge	As	Se	Br	Kr
	Rb	Sr	In	Sn	Sb	Te	I	Xe
	Cs	Ba	Tl	Pb	Bi	Po	At	Rn

Thus, members of a single family all have the same number of valence electrons and will typically lose (becoming positively charged) or gain (becoming negatively charged) the same number of electrons.

When forming simple ionic compounds the typical charges taken by these elements allow us to predict the formula of the resulting compound. Thus, sodium chloride has a formula of NaCl since it is neutral and each Na is a plus one and each Cl is a negative one. Sodium oxide has a formula of Na_2O since it is neutral and each Na is a plus one but each oxygen is a negative two requiring two sodium atoms to neutralize the negative two oxygen charge.

$$Na^+ \quad Cl^- \qquad\qquad 2Na^+ \quad O^{-2}$$

As noted before, where there is a loss or gain of electrons, the resulting compounds are called ionic compounds and the associated bonds connecting the atoms are called ionic bonds. Atoms that have given up electrons becoming positively charged, such as Na^+ and Sr^{+2} are called **cations**. Atoms that take on electrons becoming negatively charged such as Br^{-1} and O^{-2} are called **anions**.

In general, those elements that tend to give up electrons, that is become cations, are called metals and they compose about 75% of the elements.

Those elements that tend to take on electrons forming anions are called non-metals and they reside on the extreme right of the periodic table.

Again, note that the arrangement of elements is according to the atomic number (number of protons) and NOT the atomic weight.

PERIODICITY OF THE ELEMENTS

We have already noted some periodic properties of the elements. Here we can briefly review them. Many of these properties are the result of the size of the element. In general, the smaller the atom the larger will be the energy needed to remove an electron (ionization potential, IP), energy released when an electron is added (electron affinity, EA), and the greater the tendency for an atom to attract electron density from an already formed bond (electronegativity, EN). Thus, the atomic size is **inversely** related to the EN, IP, and EA.

ATOMIC RADIUS. The **atomic radius** increases from top to bottom within any family or group because of the addition of new shells- thus Bi> Sb> As> P> N (smallest). It decreases as we move across the period table within any one period from left to right- thus Na> Mg> Al> Si> P> S> Cl> Ar (smallest).

Ionization energy or ionization potential, IP- the IP is the **energy** required to **remove** the outermost electron from a **neutral** atom in the **gaseous** state.

$$A_{(g)} + \text{Energy} \rightarrow A^+ + e^-$$

It is then the "energy term" in this equation. Its value decreases from top-to-bottom within any family or group and increases within any period as one moves from left-to-right. This trend is simply the inverse of the trend with respect to size. Large atoms are not able to hold their electrons as tightly so will have lower ionization energies. Conversely, smaller molecules hold their electrons more closely and so it takes more energy to remove its electrons so they have a higher or greater ionization potential.

Electron Affinity, EA- the EA is the energy given off when a neutral atom in the gaseous state takes on energy.

$$A_{(g)} + e^- \rightarrow A^- + \text{Energy}$$

Again, in general, the EA decreases from top-to-bottom within any family and increases within any period as one moves from left-to-right.

The **electronegativity, EN**, was developed by Linus Pauling to get some measure of the amount of electron density in an already formed bond that is attracted by the two members of that bond. In this scheme, Pauling let the fluorine atom have the largest EN value, 4. Other elements had lower values such that the values increased as one moved from left-to-right within any given period and decreases for elements as one moves from top-to-bottom within any family or group. The higher the EN value assigned to an element, the generally greater its tendency to attract electrons. Conversely, the lower the EN value, the lower the tendency for that element to attract electrons within a bond. Again, the property is the inverse of size. Thus, for carbon with an EN value of about 2.5, a bond formed between C and F would have the electron density of that bond closer to the F than the C making the bond polar with the F having a partially negative charge, because of the greater electron density, and the C having a partially positive charge, because of the lesser electron density.

Another periodic property is the charge a given family of elements generally takes when they form ionic compounds. This was discussed above.

NAMING OF SIMPLE (BINARY) COMPOUNDS

We will look at the naming of two separate groups of compounds. The naming of these two separate groups is different and we need to be able to recognize which compounds belong to which grouping. One group is composed of compounds that contain metal atoms and the second group is composed of compounds that do not contain metal atoms, that is, they are composed of only non-metal atoms.

Naming- Divide into two groups.

   Binary ionic -composed of a main group metal and non-metal and
   Binary Inorganic or molecular- composed of two non-metals

Binary ionic- Give the name of the metal (these names generally with an "ium" ending such as sodium, potassium, barium and aluminum) and then give the name of the non-metal generally with an "ide" ending (such as oxygen with an ide ending becomes oxide; chlorine with an "ide" ending becomes chloride). For those derived from polyatomic ions, simply give the polyatomic ion name.

You will need to go from the name to the formula and from the formula to the name. Following are some examples.

CaO	calcium oxide	$Ba(NO_3)_2$	barium nitrate
AlN	aluminum nitride	Na_3PO_4	sodium phosphate
$NaCl$	sodium chloride	$LiBr$	lithium bromide
KOH	potassium hydroxide	$CaCO_3$	calcium carbonate
$Ba(NO_3)_2$	barium nitrate	$AlCl_3$	aluminum chloride

Binary molecular Binary inorganic compounds are composed of two non-metals. Here you need to give the number of atoms of each element (Table 3.1) along with the name of the first and then the number and name of the second element with an "ide" ending. If the first element is present only once in the formula then the prefix "mono" is often not needed. But, for the second element, even if it is presence only once in the formula the prefix "mono" must be given. Thus for SO_2 we have sulfur (no change in the ending and no need to place "mono") and for oxygen we change this to oxide and since there are two oxygen atoms we have dioxide. The name is then sulfur dioxide. For SO we have sulfur monoxide because while we have only one oxygen atom, it is the second atom and we need to include the prefix "mono."

Table 3.1 *Prefixes used in naming binary inorganic compounds.*

Number of atoms	Prefix	Number of atoms	Prefix
1	mono-	6	hexa-
2	di-	7	hepta-
3	tri-	8	octa-
4	tetra-	9	nona-
5	penta-	10	deca-

Examples follow.

NO	nitrogen monoxide	SO_3	sulfur trioxide
N_2O_4	dinitrogen tetraoxide	$ClBr_5$	chlorine pentabromide
CO	carbon monooxide	CO_2	carbon dioxide

There are some polyatomic ions that you need to memorize the name, formula, and electronic charge of (Table 3.2). These are given below. All are negatively charged **anions** except for ammonium which is a positively charged **cation**.

Table 3.2 *Names and formula of important polyatomic ions.*

Name	Formula	Name	Formula
Acetate	$C_2H_3O_2^{-1}$	Ammonium	NH_4^{+1}
Carbonate	CO_3^{-2}	Hydroxide	OH^{-1}
Nitrate	NO_3^{-1}	Phosphate	PO_4^{-3}
Sulfate	SO_4^{-2}	Acetate	$C_2H_3O_2^{-1}$

In naming the sample compounds begin by asking the question "Does it contain a metal?". If it does then you need to simply name the metal and then the non-metal with an ide ending. The exception to this is the polyatomics such as the hydroxide and sulfate. Here, the polyatomic name is used which may or may not have an ide ending. Thus, sodium hydroxide is simply NaOH. Potassium sulfate is K_2SO_4. Barium carbonate is $BaCO_3$. Ammonium nitrate is NH_4NO_3.

Many compounds have common names such as H_2O is water and CH_4 is methane. Some of these you will be expected to know such as water and ammonium. But, most you will be given and you need not memorize. Thus, a question may say, give the molar mass for acetone, C_3H_6O, so you need not know the formula for acetone since it is given to you.

MIXTURES

Most natural, real materials are really mixtures. Thus, the water in the ocean has various salts, dispersed organics and inorganics, and mostly water. The air we breathe is a mixture. **Mixtures** are combinations of materials that can be separated by physical means into two or more substances. **Heterogeneous mixtures** consist of physically distinct parts, each with different properties. Examples are crushed glass and sugar. When this mixture is added to water, the sugar will dissolve leaving the solid glass. **Homogeneous mixtures**, solutions, are mixtures that are uniform in their proportions throughout the sample. An example is common sugar dissolved in water. The sugar solution has the same amount of sugar in the top and bottom and middle of the solution. Evaporate off the water and you will have sugar remaining. There are other different kinds of mixtures including suspensions. **Suspensions** are seemingly homogeneous mixtures where the different components are in different phases like poly(vinyl acetate) in water that forms the basis for the latex paints. Essentially the poly(vinyl acetate) exists as suspended particles in water. Milk is another example where the fats and proteins are suspended in water.

Atomic Models

SENSED BUT NOT SEEN

In science, at the atomic level we may not have seen a particular item or event but we see, often with instruments, the consequences or indications that this item or event is real. A little story about our Garbage Man might put into focus some of what we will be dealing with. We moved into our neighborhood and asked our neighbors what to do with our unwanted boxes, trash, and garbage. They said to call 544-6770 which was the number of a local garbage collecting agency.

Evidence- Neighbors

We called the number and a person answered saying "Hello, this is the ACME Garbage Collecting Company."

Evidence- We called the number, and the person answered saying, "Hello, this is the ACME Garbage Collecting Company." Thus, the reply was consistent with there being a garbage collecting company.

We asked them to put us on their list to pick up the garbage. They said they came early on Tuesdays and Thursdays and we were to have the garbage curbside Monday and Wednesday evening if we wanted it picked up. So we put it out on Monday evening. Tuesday morning we got up and the trash bins were empty and the cardboard boxes missing.

Evidence- Trash missing as advertised.

We had not yet seen the garbage man but evidence for his/her existence accumulated.

Next, we heard on each Tuesday and Thursday morning noise consistent with the presence of a dump truck and the garbage being taken by the trash men.

Evidence- truck noise and talking.

We received a bill for garbage collecting service.

Evidence- received bill.

We were still not completely sure there was a garbage man so we went out early one Tuesday morning with a flashlight. At about 5 am we heard a truck drive up and the shadow of two people getting out of the truck and grapping our trash bin and dumping it into the back of the truck.

Evidence- we saw the shadow of the garbage men/women but have not actually seen them.

This is the way it is with the subatomic particles- electrons, protons, and neutrons. We see evidence that they are real and behave in a certain manner but we have never actually "seen" them.

STRUCTURE OF THE ATOM

Atoms are composed of three basic or fundamental particles. These particles are described in Table 4.1.

Table 4.1 *Basic particles of an atom.*

Name Symbol	Charge	Relative mass	Where located
ELECTRON e	negative one	1	about nucleus
PROTON p	positive one	1800	in nucleus
NEUTRON n	neutral	1800	in nucleus

As shown below, the massive protons and neutrons are contained within in central core called the nucleus while electrons exist around the nucleus.

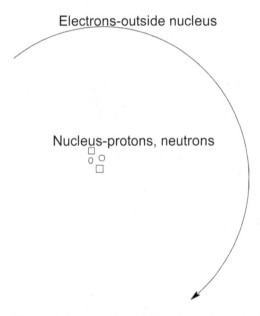

Figure 4.1 *llustration of the subatomic composition of an atom.*

There are some important definitions. These include the following.
Nucleons- protons and neutrons.
Atomic number- number of protons in the nucleus of an atom.
Mass number- total number of protons and neutrons in the nucleus of an atom.
Atomic mass unit (amu) - mass equal to one-twelfth the mass of a carbon isotope 12 which has an amu of 12.
Atomic weight - is the number of protons plus the natural abundance-average number of neutrons.
The "natural abundance-average" simply means that in nature most elements exist with some of the atoms having different numbers of neutrons but the same number of protons. Since they have the same number of protons they are the same element but since they have differing numbers of neutrons they have different masses and they are given the name isotopes. **Isotopes** are atoms of the SAME element that differ in the number of neutrons. For example

hydrogen has three isotopes- ALL have one proton, one has no neutrons, one has one neutron, and one has two neutrons. The isotope with no neutrons and only a protons is called protium since it has only a proton. The isotope with one proton and one neutron is called deuterium since it has two nuclear particles in its nucleus. The isotope with one proton and two neutrons is called tritium since it has three total nuclear particles.

Most other isotopes have no separate name but are simply described by the element name and the mass of the particular isotope. Thus carbon 12 describes the isotope that contains 6 protons and 6 neutrons in its nucleus. Carbon 13 describes the isotope that contains 6 protons and 7 neutrons. We can calculate the atomic weight of a given element when supplied with the element's isotopes and fraction (generally given in percentages that need to be divided by 100 to convert the percentages to fractions) of each isotope.

For carbon that has 98.9% carbon 12 and 1.1% carbon 13 its atomic weight is calculated as follows: $0.989 \times 12 + 0.011 \times 13 = 11.87 + 0.14 = 12.01$.

Silicon has three isotopes, Si-28 that is present in 92%; Si-29 present in 5%, and Si-30 present in 3%. The atomic weight is calculated as follows:

Atomic weight $= 28 \times 0.92 + 29 \times 0.05 + 30 \times 0.03 = 25.76 + 1.45 + 0.90 = 28.11$.

We also use other illustrations to describe the number of protons and neutrons. Many of these are of the form

^{m}X where m is the mass number and X is the chemical symbol. The **mass number** is the number of protons and neutrons. Thus for an atom that has 8 protons and 7 neutrons we would have

^{15}O and if we specify that the atom is neutral we know that the number of electrons and protons is the same.

Give the number of electrons, protons, and neutrons for ^{35}Cl if it is neutral. Being neutral means that the atom has no net charge so that the number of protons and electrons is the same. The atom is chlorine, Cl, so it has 17 protons and since it is neutral the same number of electrons, 17. The 35 refers to the mass number which is the number of protons and neutrons, that is mass number $= p + n$. We can subtract "p" from both sides and get mass number $- p = n$. For the present problem this is $35 - 17 = 18$ neutrons.

ELECTRONS AND BONDING

Interestingly, even though we have three subatomic particles, only the outer electrons are dealt with extensively in chemistry. Why? Because it is the sharing and loss/gain of electrons that form chemical bonds. Bonding can be of two kinds- **ionic** bonding where electrons are **lost** by one atom and **gained** by another; and **covalent** bonding where electrons are **shared** between two atoms.

We have not seen an electron but have seen its actions as noted before.

As noted elsewhere, there are two main kinds of chemical bonding. When electrons are exchanged, with one atom gaining an electron(s) and another giving up electron(s), columbic forces act to hold the positively and negatively atoms together forming what is called **ionic bonds**. This bonding occurs when the electronegatives, tendency to hold on to electrons, are sufficiently different between the atoms so that one atom "steals" and electron(s) from another atom. Ionic bonding often occurs when metals are paired with non-metals with the metals giving up electrons and the non-metals taking on electrons. Thus, for NaCl, the metal Na gives up an electron, becoming positively charged, to the non-metal chlorine giving chlorine an additional electron and a net negative charge. We can illustrate this with two half reactions as follows.

$$Na \rightarrow Na^{+1} + e^{-1} \quad \text{or} \quad \text{simply } Na \rightarrow Na^+ + e^- \text{ and}$$

$$Cl + e^- \rightarrow Cl^-$$

When the tendency to hold on to electrons is similar the two atoms forming the bond share the electrons forming a **covalent bond**. Thus, the tendency to hold on to electrons is similar for hydrogen and oxygen and the bonds formed between the hydrogen atoms and oxygen are covalent bonds.

LIGHT

We think of light as being what we see, but visible light is only a part of the entire light spectrum. Light is a form of energy and is described in terms of wavelength and frequency as

$$E = h\nu \text{ and } \nu = c/\lambda \text{ and substitution gives } E = hc/\lambda.$$

Wavelength is the distance between any two adjacent identical points of a wave-unit of length such as meters or nanometers. **Frequency** is the number of wavelengths of a wave that passes a fixed point in one unit of time such as the number/second is called hertz (Hz), h = Plank's constant, c = velocity of light.

You need to know that as energy increases, frequency increases- that is, energy and frequency are directly related; and that as energy increases, wavelength decreases- that is, energy and wavelength are **inversely** or **"indirectly" related**. **"Directly related"** means that as one value increases the other value increases; and as one decreases the other decreases. **Inversely related** means that as one value increases the other value does the opposite, decreases; and as one decreases the other increases. What is the relationship between frequency and wavelength?

Light is continuous ranging from high energy gamma and X-ray to low energy radio, radar, and microwaves. This continuum is often called the **ELECTROMAGNETIC SPECTRUM** and is shown in Figure 4.2.

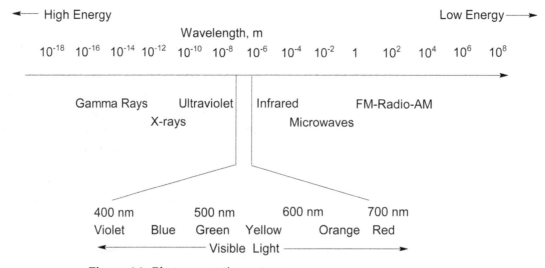

Figure 4.2 *Electromagnetic spectrum.*

Light possess, just as an electron, dual properties of acting as a particle and as a wave. Wave properties are described in terms of wavelength which is the distance needed for the wave to begin to repeat. Below, the distance between A → A, and B → B and C → C are each one wavelength. The picture represents two repeating wave units or two wavelengths.

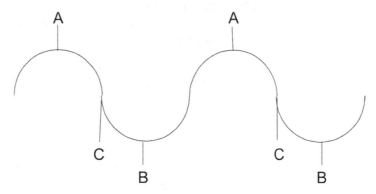

Figure 4.3 *Two cycles of a sin wave.*

When light acts as a particle we talk about it as photons.

As scientists were striking atoms with various particles and energies, they found that

- only selected, certain, specific energies were being "accepted" (absorbed)
- only certain, specific energies were being "given off" (emitted)

Einstein and others reasoned that light was not simply a continuous wave but rather could be also described as possessing bundles or quanta of photons or particles of electromagnetic energy.

From this, and many other observations, was developed the Bohr Theory of the hydrogen atom. The Bohr Theory was later transferred to other atoms. While no longer a current theory, many of the aspects of the Bohr atom are still correct. These include

- electrons have only certain, specific energy values in an atom. These allowed energy values are called **ENERGY LEVELS** and the difference correspond to the selected, specific energies that experimentally were found to be absorbed or emitted.

- electrons can move from one energy level to another when they accept (absorb; moving from an inner to an outer or further away from the nucleus energy level) or emit (moving from an outer to an inner or closer to the nucleus energy level). They cannot move to ½ or 1/3 between the energy levels but must move between one and another energy level. Absorption occurs when the correct energy is taken on to move an electron from a lower energy to a higher energy level. Emission of energy occurs when the correct energy is given off as an electron moves from a higher energy level to a lower energy level. This "correct energy" corresponds to the difference in energy between the two energy levels.

WAVE NATURE OF LIGHT

There are some general behavior ideas connected with light that are important to be reminded of.

1. Light moves at a constant speed-the speed of light -3×10^8 m/s. Energy differences are not related to speed but to frequency and the wavelength of the light. Light has both wave (frequency, wavelength) and particle (bundles) properties.

2. Planck believed that atoms in a solid oscillated or vibrated with a specific frequency and that these vibrating atoms could only have certain energies that were described by

$$E = nh\nu \text{ where } n = 1,2,3, \ldots \text{ And } h = \text{Plank's constant.}$$

3. Bohr's model was "one dimensional" whereas the Quantum Mechanical Model is three dimensional. Bohr's model concentrated on hydrogen and the Principle Quantum Number "n". In Quantum Mechanics, "n" is called the Principle Quantum Number and it describes the general distance and energy electrons within a "shell" are from the nucleus.

Heisenberg showed that it was impossible to know both the EXACT energy and EXACT location of an electron. This is called the **Heisenberg Uncertainty Principle**. Quantum Mechanics selected to know the exact energy and let the location be known in a probability manner. We call the locations of electrons **orbitals**, describing an orbital as a portability pathway of an electron. As a side note, we were told that we could not see atoms because of the uncertainty principle, yet today we can "see" them. How is this possible?

QUANTUM NUMBERS

There are four quantum numbers similar to an address in a letter to Albert as follows:

Dr. Albert Einstein
322 Cottage Street
Princeton, NJ 08540

There are four locators, beginning with the most general NJ → Princeton → 322 Cottage Street → and finally to the specific person, Albert. See how the four quantum numbers are similar to Albert's address.

To describe the (probable) location of an electron about an atomic nucleus we use FOUR quantum numbers. The combination of these four quantum numbers allows us to describe the probable location and shape of the orbital. This probability location or "wave function" of the electron is called an ATOMIC ORBITAL. We define the atomic orbital as the **probability** path taken by an electron and this atomic orbital is defined by a unique set of four quantum numbers.

These four quantum numbers are a series of values each one describing one aspect of an electron. They are described following.

1. **Principle quantum number**- given the symbol "n"; it describes the **"general" distance** from the nucleus that the particular electron resides. Each value is either a small whole number, starting with 1, or a capital

letter beginning with K. The numerical values must be **small whole positive numbers** and as the values increase, the electron, on the average, resides further from the nucleus. Each single principle quantum number describes a "**shell.**"

Numeral value	1	2	3	4	5	6	....
Letter value	K	L	M	N	O	P	....

This is the same quantum number that Bohr used in his relationship $E = nh\nu$.

Electrons with the same principle quantum number are said to be in the same shell.

2. **Angular momentum quantum number** or **second quantum number**- is given the symbol of "1". It gives the general **shape** of the orbital. Values are again given in two formats. First, values are gotten from the principle quantum number with the highest, and furthest away from the nucleus, being "n – 1" but beginning with "0", i.e., **1 = n − 1 ....0**. They are also given in small letters.

Angular momentum quantum numbers

Numeral value	Letter	Shape of orbital
0	s	Spherical
1	p	Dumb bell or two lobed
2	d	Cloverleaf (4 of 5)
3	f	
4	g	
5	h	

Each of these angular momentum quantum numbers corresponds to what is called a "**subshell.**" A subshell is a grouping of similarly shaped orbitals. The "s" type orbitals are spherical (hence the "s"); "p" type of orbitals are dumbbell shaped and most of the "d" types of orbitals are clover leafed in shape.

The shapes are probability contours. Often 90, 95, or 99% contours are given meaning that 90, 95, or 99% of the time the electron should be found within this volume.

We often use the combination of the principle and secondary quantum numbers to designate a particular subshell. Thus, an electron in the second shell and within the "O" or "s" subshell is called a "2s" electron. Similarity, an electron in the third shell with a subshell value of "1" corresponding to a "p" type of orbital is described as a "3p" electron.

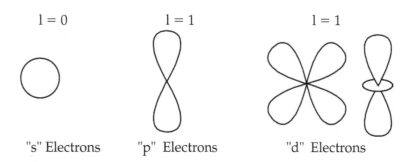

Figure 4.3 *Probability shapes of s, p, and d orbitals.*

3. The third quantum number is the **magnetic quantum number** designated by "m_i". It tells us the **number of orbitals** within each subshell. Since we will shortly know that each orbital can have 1 or 2 electrons we know the maximum number of electrons that can be in each kind of orbital, i.e., subshell.

The values for m_i are derived from "l" so that $m_i = +/- 1 ...... 0$. Thus, for "l" = 3 we have for $m_i = +/-3, +/-2, +/-1, 0$ or $-3, -2, -1, 0, 1, 2, 3$ for a total of 7 orbitals or a maximum 14 electrons (7 orbitals times 2 electrons/orbital). Also, for "l" = 3, we are talking about "f" orbitals.

4. The fourth quantum number is called the **spin quantum number** and it specifies a **specific electron** and is given the symbol m_s. Values are $m_s = +/- ½$ or $½$ and $^-½$. Thus, within a single orbital we can have one electron with a $+ ½$ spin and a second with a $-½$ spin for a total of two electrons per orbital.

The **Pauli Exclusion Principle** says that no two electrons in the same atom can have the same four quantum numbers. In other words, it says that each electron in an atom has its own unique set of four quantum numbers.

Summary: There are four quantum numbers. Each electron in every atom has its own unique set of four quantum numbers. The Pauli Exclusion Principle states that no two electrons in the same atom can have the same four quantum numbers. Each of these four quantum numbers tells something different about an electron. The principle number, n, tells the average distance that the electron resides from the nucleus of the atom. It has values of 1,2,3,4,5, ... but not zero and the larger the n number the further away from the nucleus the electron is. Each "n" value is called a **shell**. The secondary quantum number, l, tells the shape of the probable orbital. It has values of n−1 down to zero. (In quantum numbers, zero is a real value and does not mean nothing.) Each "l" value is a **subshell**. These "l" values have two names, one a number that does include zero, and a small letter. We need to know both so that when we are given one we can give the second, so for l = 0 we are talking about "s" electrons and when we are talking about "p" electrons l = 1.

The third quantum number, m_l, gives the orientation in space that each of these orbitals have and consequently tells the number of each type of orbital. m_l values are $+/-1 ..... 0$. Thus, for l = 3 we have $+/-3, +/-2, +/-1,$ and 0 or $-3, -2, -1, 0, +1, +2, +3$ or five orbitals. Each "l" value describes an **orbital**. Thus, whenever we have a combination of the principle quantum number with the secondary quantum number, like 2s, we know that there is one 2s orbital. For a 4d combination we have a possible 5 orbitals in the "n" shell.

The fourth quantum number, spin quantum number, m_s, has a value of either $+1/2$ or $-1/2$. This is often written as $+/-1/2$. This gives the maximum number of electrons that can be in any orbital. From this we can deduce the number of possible s, p, d, f, ... electrons in a given subshell.

l =	0	1	2	3	4	5	6	....
	s	p	d	f	g	h	I	....
# Orbitals	1	3	5	7	9	11	13	
Max. # Electrons	2	6	10	14	18	22	26	

Following is a brief summary of possible values for first three principle quantum numbers.

n	l(type orbital)	m_i	# orbitals/max. # electrons
1	0(s)	0	1/2
2	0(s)	0	1/2
2	1(p)	$+/-1, 0$	3/6
3	0(s)	0	1/2
3	1(p)	$+/-1, 0$	3/6
3	2(d)	$+/-2, +/-1, 0$	5/10

ELECTRONIC CONFIGURATIONS

Will often give the four quantum numbers as __, __, __, __ where the first blank is for the principle quantum number, second blank for the section quantum number, third blank for the magnetic or third quantum number and the last blank for the spin quantum number. Thus the set 2,1,0,−½ describes a 2p electron.

We will use two types of electronic configuration diagrams or notations to describe the electrons present in various elements.

Following is an easy way to memorize the order of electron types **after** the electrons are added. Notice for n = 1 there is one type of orbital, the "s" orbital which is one subshell. For n = 2 there are two types of orbitals or two subshells, the s and the p. For n = 3 there are three types of orbitals or three subshells. Etc. The number of types of orbitals is also the number of subshells.

n = 1	1s
n = 2	2s 2p
n = 3	3s 3p 3d
n = 4	4s 4p 4d 4f
n = 5	5s 5p 5d 5f 5g
n = 6	6s 6p 6d 6f 6g 6h
n = 7	7s 7p _____
n = 8	8s _____

But, electrons are added in another order that is easily remembered by simply taking the diagonals of this same triangle as shown below.

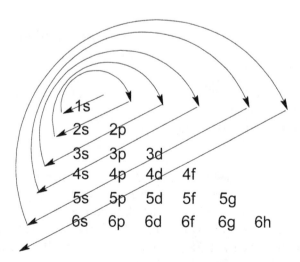

1s>2s>2p>3s>3p>4s>3d>4p
>5s>4d>5p>6s>4f>5d

This is an easy way to remember the ORDER OF FILLING-the diagonals. (This is the order that electrons are added in what is called the Aufbau or Orderly Building Up process.)

It also gives the ORDER AFTER FILLING which is simply the horizontal lines. Each horizontal line is a SHELL WITH THE SAME PRINCIPLE QUANTUM NUMBER.

Each number-letter grouping is a subshell with the same principle quantum number and same secondary quantum number. Thus a 5d has n = 5 and "l" = 2. For a 4p we have n = 4 and "l" = 1.

This triangle is also useful in assisting us to remember other aspects of electronic configurations. Following are examples of information easily obtained from the triangle.

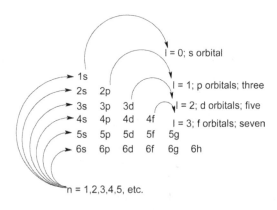

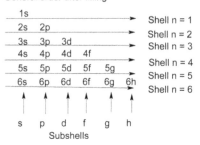

General order after filling

1s				
2s	2p			
3s	3p	3d		
4s	4p	4d	4f	
5s	5p	5d	5f	5g
6s	6p	6d	6f	6g	6h

General order after filling

1s						Shell n = 1
2s	2p					Shell n = 2
3s	3p	3d				Shell n = 3
4s	4p	4d	4f			Shell n = 4
5s	5p	5d	5f	5g		Shell n = 5
6s	6p	6d	6f	6g	6h	Shell n = 6

$1s^2$

$2s^2$ $2p^6$

$3s^2$ $3p^6$ $3d^{10}$

$4s^2$ $4p^6$ $4d^{10}$ $4f^{14}$

$5s^2$ $5p^6$ $5d^{10}$ $5f^{14}$ $5g^{18}$

6s   6p   6d   6f   6g   6h

Maximum number of electron in each subshell

The "order" of filling, or the order to which electrons are added to an atom is found using the diagonals, as noted above, giving the order as 1s> 2s>2p>3s>3p>4s>3d>4p>5s>4d>5p>6s> 4f>5d>6p>7s>5f ....

We know that each orbital can have one or two electrons. We also know that within each subshell, each "l" value, within an atom that there are possible 2 times the number of orbitals and that there are one "s" orbital with a maximum 2 "s" electons; there are three "p" orbitals with a maximum of 3×2 or 6 "p" electrons; and that there are 4 "d" orbitals with a maximum of 10 "d" electrons … Thus, we can write the electronic notations for any atom.

$$Na = 1s^2\, 2s^2\, 2p^6\, 3s^1$$

The total number of electrons for Na is 11. The number of total electrons is simply the sum of the superscripts or $2 + 2 + 6 + 1 = 11$.

The loss of one electron gives the sodium cation or $Na^+ = 1s^2\, 2s^2\, 2p^6$ which is simply a "Ne core" with 10 electrons. Na^+ and Ne are ISOELECTRONIC meaning they have the same number of electrons—but NOT protons.

$$F = 1s^2\, 2s^2\, 2p^5$$

The total number of electrons for F is 9, that is $2 + 2 + 5$

$$F^- = 1s^2\, 2s^2\, 2p^6$$

Or simply the "Ne core" and it is also isoelectronic with Na^+ and Ne.

ORBITAL DIAGRAMS

The second type of electronic diagram is a group of circles or boxes or here slots, each circle/box/slot representing an ORBITAL (with a specific n, l & m quantum number set) and each grouping is a SUBSHELL (with a specific n & l quantum number combination).

Electrons are designated as ARROWS, with the particular spin noted by the DIRECTION OF THE ARROW—either pointed up or pointed down.

1s	2s	2p	3s	3p
—	—	— — —	—	— — —

4s		3d	4p	5s
—		— — — — —	— — —	—

	4d			
	— — — — —			

HUND'S RULE of maximum multiplicity states that as electrons are added WITHIN a SUBSHELL, the SUBSHELL is HALF-FILLED BEFORE ANOTHER ELECTRON IS ADDED TO AN ORBITAL THAT ALREADY HAS AN ELECTRON. These electrons are of the same spin, until a second electron is added to the orbital.

1s	2s	2p	3s	3p
—	—	— — —	—	— — —

HYDROGEN
   HELIUM

      LITHIUM
         BERYLLIUM

            BORON
               CARBON
                  NITROGEN
                     OXYGEN
                        FLUORINE
                           NEON
                              SODIUM
                                 MAGNESIUM

ALUMINUM
SILICON
PHOSPHORUS
SULFUR
CHLORINE
ARGON

4s	3d	4p
—	— — — — —	— — —

POTASSIUM
CALCIUM
SCANDIUM
TITANIUM
VANADIUM
CHROMIUM-exception-steals 4s electron, adds it to 3d
MANGANESE
IRON
COBALT
NICKEL
COPPER-exception as Cr-steals 4s, adds to 3d
ZINC
GALLIUM
GERMANIUM
ARSENIC
SELENIUM
BROMINE
KRYPTON

EXCEPTIONS—Greater stability is found when a subshell becomes 1/2 or fully filled. This mainly works for subshells that are not "s" subshells.

ELECTRON SPIN

We have already looked at the fourth or last quantum number. Here we will look at some added relationships. Those materials that are slightly repelled by a strong magnet, like cloth, chalk, and wood, are said to be **DIAMAG-NETIC**. They normally have no unpaired electrons. Those materials, such as many metals, that are attracted to a magnet are called **PARAMAGNETIC**. These attractions are generally weak but when strong the materials are said to be **FERROMAGNETIC** and include aluminum, nickel, iron, and cobalt. These materials contain unpaired electrons or half filled orbitals. He, Ca, Ne, Sr, Zn, and Kr have no unpaired electrons. Many elements have orbitals that are not completely filled. These unfilled orbitals have only one of the possible two maximum electrons in them so they are said to be unfilled, or half filled and the electron is said to be unpaired since it does not have a second electron in its orbital.

SUN TANS AND UV RADIATION

It is easy to become sunburned because each photon of UV light that hits us releases its energy as it hits our skin. The energy is not readily dissipated because skin is an insulator. It remains near or on the skin level causing photo-excitation which we see in the form of sunburn.

If we insist in sitting in the sunlight we need to protect ourselves. We can reflect the light such as sunglasses do, but we do not want to run about with a large sunglass about us. Or, we can apply a material that will absorb the light before it gets to our skin. Suntan lotions today proclaim that they stop the harmful UV rays in the a, b, or a and b ranges. UV radiation is fairly broad occurring in a wavelength range from 100 to 400 nm. These energies are sufficiently energetic to break bonds in our skin resulting in unwanted results. Remember that energy and wavelength are inversely related so that a lower wavelength such as 200 nm is more energetic and more dangerous than radiation at 300 nm. The UV range has been subdivided into three ranges. UV-a is the range of 320–400 nm. UV radiation in this range have the energy to penetrate our outermost layer of skin causing damage to the surface layer and to some of the layers beneath it resulting in premature aging, sagging, wrinkles, and skin cancer. UV-b has wavelengths in the range of 290–320 and is more dangerous because it is more energetic. It causes photolytic cleavage of the skin's proteins causing sun burn. It also inhibits DNA and RNA replication which is why overexposure to UV-b leads to skin cancer. UV-c in the range of 100–290 nm is even more energetic but fortunately it is largely filtered out by the ozone layer or we would have lots more skin cancer. This explains why we are so concerned with the possible loss of the ozone layer. Without it, we are in trouble.

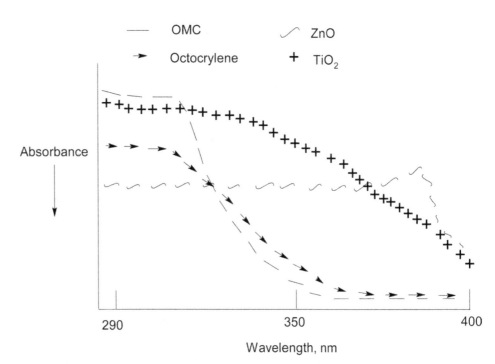

Figure 4.4 *Plot of ability of suntan lotions to protect against UV radiation as a function of UV wavelength.*

Above, Figure 4.4, is a plot of the amount of UV radiation absorbed by different suntan lotions. The greater the absorption by the suntan lotion the greater the protection against that particular wavelength. Today there are a number of new ingredients in suntan lotions that offer greater protection over a wider range. Thus, some suntan lotions have titanium dioxide, TiO_2, as an ingredient that allows protection over the entire UV range. Pay attention to the ingredients of the suntan lotion you are using.

Thus, all types of UV can cause trouble and it is most important, since we still have the ozone layer, to get protection for UV-b radiation since it is more energetic and dangerous.

MELANIN

Radiation is also important in the synthesis and rearrangement of important "surface" macromolecules on our skin. Our skin color occurs because of the presence of melanin. At least two colored melanins are formed—a series of black melanins and a series of so-called red melanins. Our skin pigmentation is determined by the relative amounts of these red and black melanins in our skin. Albinos do not have melanins in their skin so are white. Melanin also acts as the tanning agent. As UV radiation hits our skin it acts to encourage the melanin molecules to grow resulting in a deepening brown coloration that acts to help shield our skin from potential damage. Melanin does not have a precise structure, but rather it has an average or general structure as pictured in Figure 4.5.

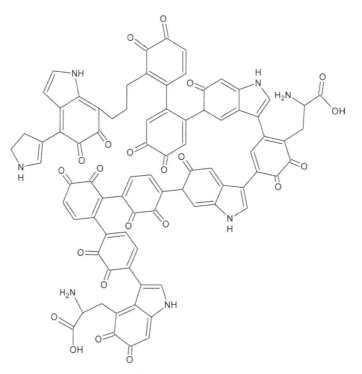

Figure 4.5 *Representative structure of melanin.*

The concentration of melanin also contributes to the color of our hair (except for redheads where the iron-rich pigment trichosiderin dominates). The bleaching of hair, generally achieved through exposure to hydrogen peroxide, is a partial result of the oxidation of the melanin. A side reaction of bleaching is the formation of more sulfur crosslinks leading to bleached hair being more brittle because of the increased crosslinking leading to a decrease in hair flexibility.

Melanin also provides a dark background in our eye's iris, is involved in animal color changes (such as the octopus and chameleon), is formed when fruit is bruised, and is partially responsible for the coloration of tea.

The Atomic Nucleus

RADIOACTIVITY

Many elements have isotopes and often these isotopes are unstable and emit particles. The process of emitting these particles is called **radioactivity**. Here we will restrict our attention to three of these particles, the alpha, beta, and gamma particles.

Alpha particle— two protons and two neutrons, really a helium atom without its electrons so it has a +2 charge; He^{+2}. The alpha particle does not easily penetrate solids because of its relatively high mass and size. But because of its great energy it can do great damage to us; travel only short, cm, distances before they pick up electrons to become a helium atom. Has a health factor of 1 rad.

$$\text{Alpha, a, particle} \longrightarrow \text{Paper}$$

Beta particle— an electron, thus it has a -1 charge, e^{-1}; faster than alpha particles; penetrate light materials such as paper, clothing and into our skin killing cells near the surface; generally more harmful to us than beta particles. Has a health factor of 10 rad.

$$\text{Beta, b, particle} \longrightarrow \text{Paper} \longrightarrow \text{Aluminum}$$

Gamma rays— high energy rays without any charge and only the $E = mc^2$ type of mass; are able to penetrate most materials; can harm external (skin) as well as internal (organ) cells; dangerous in any quantity.

$$\text{Gamma , g, rays} \longrightarrow \text{Paper} \longrightarrow \text{Aluminum} \longrightarrow \text{Lead}$$

Each particle has its own assigned health factor. For the alpha and beta particles this health factor must be related to distance from the source as well as protective material that is between the source and you. Thus, it is customary to wear badges that register the radiation. The lethal dose of radiation begins at about 500 rems. A **rad** is the **Radiation Absorbed Dose** and one rad = 0.01 joule of radiation absorbed per kilogram of tissue. The **rem** is the **roentgen equivalent man**. It measures the ability of radiation to do harm.

$$\textbf{Rem} = \text{radiation dosage} \times \text{health factor}$$

Thus, the number of rems if hit by 100 rads of alpha radiation is 100 rad $\times$ 10 rems/rad = 1,000 rems and you are probably dead.

Radiation is used to crosslink plastic film, kill bad microorganisms in fresh foods, treatment of cancers, create energy—but in all cases it should be treated as potentially dangerous and appropriate safeguards taken.

Radioactivity comes from an imbalance in the nucleus generally when there are too many neutrons present in comparison to the protons. Thus, as a rough rule of thumb, the chance that a material will be radioactive increases as the ratio of neutrons/protons increases.

As nuclei degrade giving off particles and/or energy, it is called radioactive decay or radioactivity. It appears that there are two kinds of forces—the "normal" attraction between unlike charges that occur on a larger than nuclear space scale and the nuclear forces that occur within very tight spaces-nuclear sizes. Within the nucleus there are the repulsive tendencies because of the repulsion between the positively charged protons and the neutrons that act as a glue to hold them together. It is interesting that during radioactive decays involving decay or degradation of protons, that the element changes from one element to another because a neutron degradation produces a proton (the number of protons determine the element) and an electron.

$$n \rightarrow p^+ + e^-$$

In chemical reactions, the number and kind of atoms stays the same, but in nuclear reactions involving neutron decay (decomposition) the atomic number, number of protons, increases one for each neutron that decays. These reactions are called nuclear reactions to separate them from chemical reactions. This change from one element to another element is called **transmutation**. Elements can also lose atomic particles including clusters such as alpha (2 protons and 2 neutrons) that result in transmutation. For instance

$$^{238}U \rightarrow {}^{234}Th + {}^{4}He$$

In fact, loss of some partials such as neutrons and alpha particles can result in further nuclear reactions occurring brought about because either the mother of daughter nuclei are struck or hit by these particles causing further nuclear changes.

$$^{234}Th \rightarrow {}^{234}Pa^+ + e^-$$

Here a neutron decayed with the proton remaining and the expulsion of an electron. This cascade continues until a final stable element is formed. In the case of uranium, the final compound is lead, Pb.

You will need to be able to balance simple nuclear reactions. In these reactions the number of protons and neutrons must be the same on both sides and the net charges on each side of the $\rightarrow$ must be the same.

HALF-LIFE

The rate at which radioactive decays occur varies widely from well less than a second to thousands of years.

The rate of decay is measured in terms of what is called **half-life**, which is the time required for ½ of the particular element to decay. Again, **half-life** is simply the time required for the radioactivity of a material to reach one half of its original (whenever the initial radioactive was measured) radioactivity. Thus, if we had a material that registered 1,000 counts/second and it took 30 minutes for the number of counts to register 500 counts/second, then its half-life would be 30 minutes.

You will be expected to do simple problems associated with half-life. If the half-life of a particular radioactive material is 4 hours, how much is left after 16 hours.

Number of half-lives	0	1	2	3	4	5
Time-hours	0	4	8	12	16	20
Fraction Left	1	1/2	1/4	1/8	1/16	1/32

The answer is that 1/16 is left after 16 hours which is 4 half-lives.

The shorter the half-life the more rapidly it decays giving off its sub-atomic, nuclear particles. Radioactivity can be measured using a Geiger counter that measures the amount of a certain kind of emission that is given off in some time with units like counts/second or counts/minute.

Important factors in looking at radioactivity include
rate of decay (half-life)
decay particle(s)
distance
time of exposure

RADIOACTIVE DATING

The most widely used radioactive dating technique is radiocarbon dating. Carbon has two isotopes, C-12 which is not radioactive (it is stable) and it makes up over 99.99% of carbon and C-13 which decays. But there is also C-14 that is produced by the decay of N-14.

$$^{14}N + {}^{1}n \rightarrow {}^{14}C + {}^{1}H$$

This C-14 then decays.

$$^{14}C \rightarrow {}^{14}N + {}_{-1}e^{-}$$

Carbon-14 has a half-life of about 5730 years. Neutrons cannot penetrate very deeply so that once a person or tree is submerged below ground or water where neutrons are not able to produce any more C-14, the amount of C-14 will simply decrease so that the amount of C-14 in a person/tree allows for a measure of the length of time that material has isolated form exposure to neutrons, and presumably dead.

Radiocarbon dating is good for several to tens of thousands of years but for longer times other methods must be used. Unfortunately, these other methods do not work well dating the age of once living things.

NUCLEAR FISSION

Fission is breaking up, so nuclear fission is the breaking up of the nucleus. In much of the radioactive decay, only small chunks of the nucleus are broken off or added. But in some cases, the energy of the colliding species, such as a fast moving neutron, is sufficient to cause the nucleus to split into two large groups- that is, the nucleus is split. Nuclear reactions are normally exothermic so that energy is given off. In fact, there is a change in the overall mass which is converted into energy according the famous Einstein relationship $E = mc^2$.

Beginning $\rightarrow$ Neutron Split + Energy from Mass Change (nuclear energy)

Under certain circumstances, there is sufficient nuclear active material available, called the **critical mass**, to sustain (maintain, keep going) the nuclear reaction leading to a chain reaction. If this continues, the splitting of the nucleus (splitting of the atom) continues at even a faster rate converting more matter into energy, and BANG; a nuclear explosion.

Under controlled conditions, subcritical amounts of nuclear activity are used to make energy. Energy (heat is a form of energy) is given off from the nuclear reaction and allowed to heat water that is converted into steam to drive large turbines that produce electricity.

Most of our energy is produced from combustion (burning) fossil fuels-petroleum and coal.

$$Coal + O_2 \rightarrow CO_2 + energy$$

$$C_xH_y + O_2 \rightarrow CO_2 + H_2O + energy$$

There is no free lunch. You can't get any thing free. How are these statements related to energy?

There are many advantages of nuclear energy but also some disadvantageous. What are these?

Advantages	Disadvantageous
Relatively clean in comparison to coal	Nuclear waste is long lived
Relatively efficient	Need to get rid of nuclear waste
Not dependent on other countries	Dangerous
for supply	
_____	_____
_____	_____

We talk about tradeoffs and that we do not live in a risk free society. How are these related to our various fuels? What is a "tradeoff"?

What does a nuclear reactor going critical (such as in Russia) mean?

NUCLEAR FUSION

Fusion is bringing together. When there is sufficient energy propelling two nuclei together, the nuclei overcome the repulsions of the two positively charged nuclei and combine. This is called **nuclear fusion**. The energy to propel the nuclei together is generally supplied by heat necessary to raise the temperatures to near that of the sun. In fact, this is what is happening in our sun and how it supplies energy as light. The formation of a new nuclei results in the giving off of lots of energy that heats up the atmosphere. In general, the temperatures needed to cause thermonuclear fusion are generated by a nuclear bomb and the energies created by nuclear fusion are greater than in the nuclear fission. When uncontrolled nuclear fusion occurs, it results in a hydrogen bomb blast.

Efforts are underway to harness nuclear fusion (controlled fusion) as an energy source. It might well be the energy source for later 21st century. For the most part, only light particles are able to be heated high enough to split the atom. Thus, isotopes of atomic hydrogen are typically used. Lasers are used as sources of energy and magnets are used for containment.

One reaction that gives us the hydrogen bomb is given below where temperatures in excess of 45 million C are needed and this temperature can be supplied by an atomic bomb.

$$^2H + {}^3H \rightarrow {}^4He + {}^1n + \text{lots of energy}$$

This is also believed to be the major source of energy from the sun. Another theory regarding how the sun's energy is created involves a complex of reactions often called the carbon cycle. One of the particles involved is called the positron which can be considered a positive electron, $_1e^+$.

$$^{12}C + {}^1H \rightarrow {}^{13}N \rightarrow {}^{13}C + {}_1e^+$$

$$^{13}C + {}^1H \rightarrow {}^{14}N$$

$$^{14}N + {}^1H \rightarrow {}^{15}O \rightarrow {}^{15}N + {}_1e^+$$

$$^{15}N + {}^1H \rightarrow {}^{12}C + {}^4He$$

Bonding and Molecular Shape

BONDING

We talk about secondary and primary bonding. **Secondary bonding** involves less energetic associations between different molecules and ions. These associations are not permanent and change with time. Secondary bonding includes hydrogen bonding which is responsible for water being a liquid at room temperature. The various water molecules attract one another and a moment later these water molecules are associated with different water molecules, etc. These associations are said to be momentary. Secondary bonding will be dealt with in section 7. By comparison, **primary bonds** are more permanent so that the same hydrogen and oxygen atoms are bonded together until some chemical event occurs that causes a breakage and reforming of the oxygen and hydrogen atoms forming new combinations. They are said to be stronger bonds meaning that to overcome the attraction of the bonding atoms more energy is needed. The **bonding energy** is simply the energy needed to break a bond.

$$A - B + Energy \rightarrow A + B$$

It is the primary bonding that forms compounds. We further divide primary bonds into ionic and covalent bonding. Ionic bonding occurs when the members of the bond have quite different tendencies to hold on and attract electrons. Ionic bonds are often formed from reactions between metals and non-metals. Atoms that have lost electrons have a net positive charge and are called **cations** and those that have an excess of electrons have a negative charge and are called **anions**.

Covalent bonds are formed when the bonding pairs have similar tendencies to attract electrons. These are often formed between non-metal atoms. Whenever the bonding atoms are different there is a different tendency towards the shared electrons forming the covalent bond resulting in the atom with greater attracting tendency having a partially negative charge and the atom having a lesser ability to attract the electrons forming the bond having a partially positive charge. These unlike atoms then form bonds that have **permanent dipoles** and they are said to be **polar bonds**. More about this later.

Here we will focus on the formation of covalent bonds.

Molecular shapes are important in dictating the chemical and physical properties of molecules. Thus, molecular shape is an important consideration in chemistry. In this section we will look at how we can predict the shape of simple molecules from the number of valence electrons present in elements that make up a chemical bond.

Compounds that are largely primarily bonded through covalent bonds have molecular shapes that are dictated by the number of valence electrons. The atoms involved in the formation of covalent bonds are typically non-metals and reside in the right side of the periodic table. We can accurately describe the number of valence electrons by noting which family an element is located in. Looking at a periodic table we can describe the number of valence electrons as given in Table 6.1.

Table 6.1 *Number of valence electrons for the main group elements.*

Number of Valence Electrons 1	2	3	4	5	6	7	8
H							He
Li	Be	B	C	N	O	F	Ne
Na	Mg	Al	Si	P	S	Cl	Ar
K	Ca	Ga	Ge	As	Se	Br	Kr
Rb	Sr	In	Sn	Sb	Te	I	Xe
Cs	Ba	Tl	Pb	Bi	Po	At	Rn

Thus, members of a single family all have the same number of valence electrons and will take on the same shape when the same number of bonds is formed. As will be seen, compounds of the form H_2X that are members of the same family as oxygen are all tetrahedral/bent for the oxygen family as H_2O, H_2S, H_2Se, H_2Te, and H_2Po.

Before we begin looking at the formation of Lewis structures we will consider some definitions.

BOND LENGTH is the distance between nuclei.

$$A \text{———————} B$$

BOND ORDER is the number of shared electron PAIRS present in the bond. We can have **SINGLE** bonds (one sigma-bond),

$$A\text{—}B$$

DOUBLE bonds (one sigma and one pi-bond), and

$$A=B$$

TRIPLE bonds (one sigma and two pi-bonds).

$$A\equiv B$$

LEWIS STRUCTURES (ELECTRON-DOT STRUCTURES OR FORMULAS)

Lewis structures or **electron-dot formulas** focus on the number of bonding or valence or outer-most electrons in an atom. Here a "." represents an electron and ".." Or a "-" represents two electrons. When these electrons are shared between two atoms ".." Or "-" they represents a bond. When the ".." or "-" is not involved in bonding they are referred to as **UNBONDED electrons** or an **UNBONDED ELECTRON PAIR**. We can draw Lewis structures for both ionic and covalent compounds. Below are Lewis structures for two ionic compounds, NaCl and MgF_2.

$$Na + Cl \rightarrow Na^+ + Cl^- \rightarrow NaCl$$

$$F + Mg + F \rightarrow F^- + Mg^{+2} + F^- \text{ or } Mg + 2F \rightarrow MgF_2$$

It is more common to draw Lewis structures for covalent compounds and from them deduce the structural geometry of the central atom. Following are Lewis structures for some simple covalent bonded compounds.

$$H^\circ + H^\circ \rightarrow H\text{-}H \rightarrow H_2$$

$$H^\circ + Cl^\circ \rightarrow H\text{-}Cl$$

$$H_2 + Cl_2 \rightarrow 2HCl$$

The **OCTET RULE** says that an atom can have no more than eight (valence) electrons about it. In point of fact, only the elements in the second period follow this rule. Why? It is because the second period of elements has only 2s and 2p electrons and can accommodate only a total of eight electrons in its outer shell. By comparison, the third, fourth, etc. periods have shells that also have "d" orbitals and expansion into these "d" orbitals allows the number of outer electrons to be greater than eight.

There are two types of covalent bonds. The first bond formed is a **sigma bond**. For sigma bonds the electron density of the bond is on the bonding axis. The bonding axis is simply a line drawn between the nuclei of the two bonding atoms.

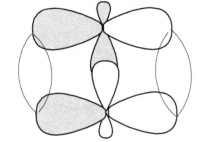
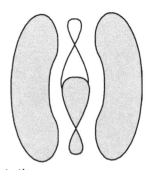

Sigma Bond   Pi Bond Representations

The **pi bond** is the name given to any additional bonds after the formation of the sigma bond. Pi bonds have the electron density about but not on the bonding axis. This is because pi bonds are often formed from the overlap of "p" and "d" orbitals that are not pointed towards one another.

In reality, bonds are not only IONIC or COVALENT—BUT they often contain BOTH types of bonding even though we will attempt to describe the bonding in terms of IONIC or COVALENT.

ELECTRONEGATIVITY

As noted before, even within a covalent bond, unless the atoms are the same, there is a tendency for one atom to attract more than their fair share (more than 50%) of the bonding electron density. These bonds are said to be polar bonds. Thus, the unequal sharing of the bonding electrons creates the polar bonds.

ELECTRONEGATIVITY is a measure of the ability of an atom in a molecule to attract bonding electrons to itself. Linus Pauling assigned Electronegativity values to atoms constructing a (relative) scale based on "fluorine" being the most electronegative, with an electronegativity, EN, value of 4. In general, the EN values decrease from top-to-bottom and increase from left-to-right. In fact, the trend is the same trend found for ionization potentials and is again inverse to size.

Through the use of comparing EN values of two atoms involved in a bond, we can predict it a bond is covalent or ionic and somewhat the extent of covalent character. Further, we can predict which atom in the bonding pair will have an excess of electron density. In general, the closer together two atoms forming the bond the more apt it will be covalent; conversely, to further away from one another, the more apt it is to be ionic.

MOLECULAR AND ELECTRON PAIR GEOMETRY

The initial step in determining the geometry of molecules is to draw a Lewis structure of the compound. Following is a simple outline that allows a Lewis Electron Dot Formula to be drawn.

1. Calculate the total number of valence or outer electrons.

2. Write a skeleton structure.

3. Distribute electrons to atoms surrounding the central atom. Use the octet rule when applicable.

4. Distribute remaining electrons as pairs.

We often will replace two electrons, two dots with a "-".

Covalent bonds are directional relying on the space taken by available contributing orbitals.

The **MOLECULAR GEOMETRY** is the (general) SHAPE of the molecule considering ONLY the atoms (the bonded electron pairs) whereas the **ELECTRON PAIR** geometry includes both the atoms (bonded electron pairs) and unbonded electron pairs. **It is important to remember that you must determine the electron pair geometry and the molecular geometry is then determined from considering the electron pair geometry.**

The **VALENCE-SHELL ELECTRON-PAIR REPULSION**, VSEPR, MODEL is a model that correctly predicts the shape of molecules in which atoms and unbonded electron pairs are kept as FAR AWAY FROM ONE ANOTHER AS POSSIBLE because of the repulsion of the nuclei and electron clouds, but they must be close enough to allow good interaction between the bonding electrons and the nuclei.

The geometry of covalent compounds is dependent on the number of valence electrons about the central atom. These electrons may be

bonded electrons and
unbonded electrons (generally unbonded electron pairs).

Here we will differentiate between the

- **ARRANGEMENT OF PAIRS (electron pair geometry)**-which considers BOTH unbonded electrons and bonded atoms
- **MOLECULAR GEOMETRY**— that considers only the arrangement of the atoms or bonded electron pairs.

Some helps.

- Determine which is the CENTRAL atom and which are the SURROUNDING atom or atoms. For simple molecules the central atom is generally the one that is there in the least number and surrounding atoms are the ones that are present in larger number.
- Write the electron dot formula concentrating on the number of electron pairs about the central atom.
- Determine the number of "BONDED" and "UN-BONDED" electron pairs about the CENTRAL atom. Count multiple (pi) bonds as only one. Each of these BONDED and UN-BONDED pairs will act as "PLACE HOLDERS" determining the overall geometry about the CENTRAL atom.

It turns out that most molecules have some symmetry in them and so we use a procedure where hybrid orbitals, equivalent bond sites are formed. Only valence electrons are involved in this hybrid formation.

Following is a summary of the general geometry shapes considering **ELECTRON PAIR GEOMETRY**—that considers **both BONDED ATOMS and UNBONDED ELECTRONS**
MOLECULAR GEOMETRY—that considers **only the ARRANGEMENT OF ATOMS**-to get the MOLECULAR GEOMETRY we must first look at the arrangement of ALL pairs of valence electrons.

Table 6.2 *Summary of geometries for various AB groups.*

AB Grouping	Electron-Pair Geometry	Molecular Geometry	Example(s)	Hybridization & Bond angle(s)
AB_2	Linear	Linear	CO_2, $BeCl_2$	sp; 180
AB_3	Triangular Planer	Triangular Planer	BF_3, H_2CO	sp^2; 120
AB_3	Triangular Planer	Bent	$GeBr_2$, $SnCl_2$	sp^2; 120
AB_4	Tetrahedral	Tetrahedral	CCl_4, $SnBr_4$, NH_4^{+1}	sp^3; 109
AB_4	Tetrahedral	Triangular Pyramidal	NH_3, PCl_3	sp^3; 109
AB_4	Tetrahedral	Bent	H_2O	sp^3; 109
AB_5	Trigangular Bipyramidal	Triangular Bipyramidal	PCl_5, SnF_5^{-1}	sp^3d; 90, 120, 180
AB_5	Trig. Bipy.	See-saw	SBr_4, SeF_4	sp^3d; 90, 120, 180
AB_5	Trig. Bipy.	"T"	IBr_3, $SbCl_3^{-2}$	sp^3d; 90, 180
AB_5	Trig. Bipy	Linear	XeI_2	sp^3d; 180
AB_6	Octahedral	Octahedral	SCl_6	sp^3d^2; 90, 180
AB_6	Octahedral	Square Pyramid	$BrCl_5$	sp^3d^2; 90, 180
AB_6	Octahedral	Square Planer	$XeBr_4$	sp^3d^2; 90, 180

Following are some examples where the geometries are determined though Lewis structures. Here, we will be more formal using the available orbitals about the central atom to govern the geometry about this central atom.

BeF_2 *Establish the central atom-Be-surrounded by two F.

(We can, at this point also generate the electron-dot arrangement and determine that the compound is <u>LINEAR</u>)

F-Be-F

*Write the electron configuration for each-Be and F.

Be	$1s^2$	$2s^2$	
F	$1s^2$	$2s^2$	$2p^5$

We need to <u>create</u> two <u>half-filled</u> orbitals on Be to overlap with the two (one each) <u>half-filled</u> orbitals on F. To do this, we <u>promote</u> or move forward one of the 2s electrons on Be to one of the 2p (unfilled) orbitals.

This gives us TWO HALF-FILLED orbitals on the Be-one half-filled 2s and one half-filled 2p orbitals.

(We will look at ONLY the valence or outer electrons)

Be $2s^1$ $2p^1$

*Since these orbitals will be the same, we <u>HYBRIDIZE</u> THE TWO ORBITALS TO GIVE <u>TWO EQUIVALENT</u> sp ORBITALS-thus two objects surrounding a third-linear. The two "F" positions are the same with a F-Be-F bond angle of 180 degrees.

Be   2sp   2sp   or   TWO 2sp orbitals

TWO F $2s^2$ $2p^5$

BF$_3$ -Boron Trifluoride
*Establish the central atom-B surrounded by three F.

(The electron-dot arrangement will have 12 electron pairs-3.5 from each F and 1.5 from B. Thus, we have three "place holders"-the F's-surrounding the B giving a trigonal planer geometry.

*Write the electron configuration for each B and F

B	$2s^2$	$2p^1$
F	$2s^2$	$2p^5$

We need to <u>create</u> THREE <u>half-filled</u> on B to overlap with the three (one each) half-orbitals on F. We do this by <u>promoting</u> or moving forward one of the 2s electrons on B to one of the UNFILLED 2p orbitals giving THREE half-filled orbitals.

B $2s^1$ $2p^1$ $2p^1$

*Since these orbitals will be the same, we <u>hybridize</u> the THREE orbitals on B giving <u>THREE EQUIVALENT</u> sp^2 ORBITALS-thus three objects surrounding a fourth-trigonal planer. All bond angles and positions are the same. All F-B-F bond angles are 120 degrees.

B   Three $2sp^2$ orbitals

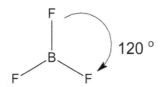

Methane-CH_4

*The central atom is C surrounded by four H. The electron-dot arrangement is <u>TETRAHEDRAL.</u>

*Write the electron configuration for each-C and H

C $2s^2$ $2p^2$
H $1s^1$

We need to <u>create</u> <u>FOUR half-filled</u> orbitals on C to overlap with the FOUR (one each) half-filled 1s orbitals on H. We <u>promote</u> ONE of the 2s electrons into the <u>UNFILLED 2p orbital</u> of C. This will give us FOUR half-filled orbitals on C.

C $2s^1$ 2p 2p 2p

*To make these orbitals equivalent, we HYBRIDIZE the <u>FOUR</u> orbitals giving <u>FOUR EQUIVALENT sp^3 ORBITALS</u>-thus-four objects about a fifth or a tetrahedral geometry. All H-C-H bond angles are about 109.5 degrees.

C   Four $2sp^3$

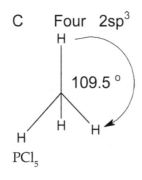

PCl_5

*The central atom is P surrounded by FIVE Cl atoms. The electron-dot arrangement is <u>TRIGONAL BIPYRAMIDAL</u>.

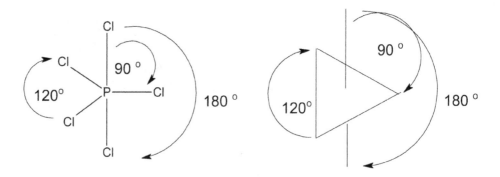

This has two equivalent environments-two "axial" and two planar. The bond angles are 120 for the planar Cl-P-Cl and 180 for the axial Cl-P-Cl

The electron configuration for P and Cl is as follows-outer electrons only

$$P \qquad 3s^2 \qquad 3p^3 \qquad 3d^0$$

$$Cl \qquad 3s^2 \qquad 3p^5$$

We need to <u>create FIVE half-filled</u> orbitals on P to overlap with FIVE (one half-filled each for five Cl's) half-filled orbitals on Cl. We do this through <u>promoting ONE 3s AND ONE 3p (ONE COUPLED 3p PAIR) ELECTRONS-ONE TO AN UNFILLED 3p ORBITAL AND ONE TO A 3d ORBITAL.</u>(Let us now concern ourselves with only the valence or bonding electrons.)

$$P \qquad 3s^1 \qquad 3p^1 \qquad 3p^1 \qquad 3p^1 \qquad 3d^1$$

*Since these orbitals are the same, we <u>hybridize</u> the five orbitals on P giving <u>FIVE EQUIVALENT</u> sp^3d orbitals.

$$P \qquad Five \qquad 3sp^3d \quad orbitals$$

SeF_6

*The central atom is Se surrounded by SIX F atoms. The electron-dot arrangement is that of an <u>OCTAHEDRAL</u>-all SIX "F" positions are equivalent-the same. Bonding angles are 180 and 90 degrees for F-Se-F.

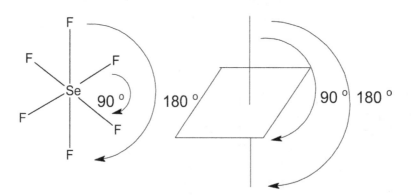

*The electron configuration for S and F is as follows-giving only the valence or bonding electrons.

$$\text{Se} \qquad 4s^2 \qquad 4p^4 \qquad 4d^0$$
$$\text{F} \qquad 2s^2 \qquad 2p^5$$

We need to <u>create</u> <u>SIX half-filled orbitals</u> on Se. We do this by moving ONE 4s and TWO 4p electrons-ONE WILL GO TO AN UNFILLED 4p ORBITAL AND TWO WILL GO TO UNFILLED 4d orbitals.

$$\text{Se} \qquad 4s^1 \qquad 4p^1 4p^1 4p^1 \qquad 4d^1 4d^1$$

*Since these SIX orbitals are the same, we <u>HYBRIDIZE</u> the <u>SIX</u> orbitals on Se giving <u>SIX EQUIVALENT</u> sp^3d^2 orbitals.

$$\text{Se} \qquad \text{Six } 4sp^3d^2 \qquad \text{orbitals}$$

The **dipole moment** is a measure of the degree of charge separation in a molecule. The greater the DIPOLE MOMENT, typically the greater the IONIC character of the bond. For SYMMETRICAL molecules where the DIPOLE MOMENTS cancel one another, the DIPOLE MOMENT is zero, even though the particular bond can be polar. Thus, there is a relationship between a molecule's DIPOLE MOMENT and its MOLECULAR GEOMETRY.

Following are examples where there are polar bonds but where the **entire** molecule is **non-polar**, does **not** have a permanent dipole or dipole moment.

$$CF_4 \qquad O=C=O \qquad BBr_3$$

Following are examples where the molecules **contain** polar bonds and where the entire molecule **is** polar and has a permanent dipole or dipole moment.

$$CO \qquad CHCl_3 \quad BBr_2Cl$$

MULTIPLE BONDING

In some cases, there may be more than one bond between the same two atoms.

The initial or first bond is **always** a <u>**SIGMA**</u> bond where the <u>electron density lays **ON** the bonding axis.</u> **Subsequent** bonds are <u>**Pi**</u> bonds where the <u>electron density lays **ABOUT** the bonding axis.</u>

Let us look at several examples.

Please remember that almost always carbon forms FOUR bonds and oxygen forms TWO bonds.

ETHYLENE, $CH_2=CH_2$

We will treat ethylene as though it has <u>TWO CARBONS that are CEN-TRAL ATOMS</u>. Here, each carbon is surrounded by two hydrogen atoms and one carbon atom. Thus, the geometry arrangement about each carbon is the SAME and it is <u>TRIGONAL PLANAR</u>. We then need <u>THREE HALF-FILLED ORBITALS ON **EACH** THE CARBON</u>. We get these by promotion of <u>ONE 2s ELECTRON TO A VACATE 2p ORBITAL</u>.

$$C \qquad 2s^2 \qquad 2p^2$$

$$C \qquad 2s^1 \qquad 2p^1\ 2p^1\ 2p^1$$

This creates <u>FOUR half-filled</u> orbitals of which only <u>THREE</u> will be used to form <u>THREE SIGMA</u> bonds. These <u>THREE HALF-FILLED ORBITALS will be hybridized forming THREE EQUIVALENT sp² orbitals.</u>

The <u>REMAINING HALF-FILLED</u> orbital on C, a p orbital, is at such an orientation that it can only overlap with a similar (left-over) half-filled orbital on the second C <u>ABOUT THE BONDING AXIS FORMING A PI BOND-THE SECOND BOND TO CARBON.</u>

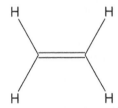

H₂CO, Formaldehyde

*The central atom is the C surrounded by two H's and one O.

Let us focus on two atoms this time-the C and O. The ground state electronic configuration is

$$C \qquad 2s^2 \qquad 2p^2$$
$$O \qquad 2s^2 \qquad 2p^4$$

The oxygen needs two half-filled orbitals-one will form a sigma bond with carbon and the second will form a pi bond with carbon- and each hydrogen needs one half filled orbital.

We need <u>THREE HALF-FILLED</u> orbitals on carbon-two to overlap, form sigma bonds, with the two hydrogens and one to overlap with the one oxygen. We form these THREE HALF-FILLED orbitals through promotion of the 2s electron to an empty 2p orbital. This generates FOUR <u>NOT</u> THREE HALF-FILLED ORBITALS ON THE CARBON ATOM. We form then three hybridized sp² orbitals-that will give us <u>THREE SIGMA</u> BONDS-ONE TO EACH OF THE TWO HYDROGENS AND ONE TO THE SINGLE OXYGEN ATOM.

We now focus on both of the remaining vacate half-filled 2p orbital on C and on the REMAINING 2p <u>VACATE unfilled orbital on oxygen. These two form a pi bond through the overlapping of the two half-filled 2p orbitals-one on C and one on O.</u>

O
Pi Bond ‖ Sigma Bonds

H   H

ACETYLENE

Here, the central atoms are the two carbons. Let us focus on only one of the carbons. We need TWO HALF-FILLED orbitals-one for the H and one for the C. We get these through promotion of one of the 2s electrons to a vacate 2p orbital of C.

$$C \qquad 2s^2 \qquad 2p^2 \qquad \rightarrow \qquad 2s^1 \qquad 2p \ 2p \ 2p$$

We will now form a hybrid of ONE 2s ORBITAL AND ONE 2p orbital. This gives us two sigma bonds-one each to the carbon and the hydrogen.

H —C— C   And for both carbons   H —C—C— H

We now draw our attention to the second C seeing that it, and the first carbon, both HAVE TWO HALF-FILLED orbitals remaining. These two remaining half-filled orbitals can overlap with the two half-filled orbitals of the second carbon forming TWO pi BONDS.

HC≡≡≡CH

The five basic electron pair geometries are given below.

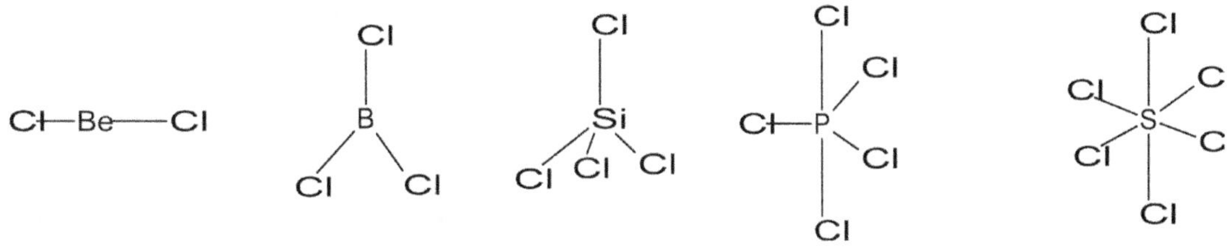

Molecular Mixing

SECONDARY BONDING

There are two groupings of bonding-one called primary-ionic/covalent/ metallic and the second, less energetic, called secondary bonding. Here we will focus on secondary bonding. While these secondary bonding types do not hold molecules together somewhat "permanently" they are responsible for dissolving compounds in different solvents as well as other important physical phenomena.

We will look at four types of secondary bonding- in decreasing strength

Ion-dipole	Strongest
Dipole-dipole	
Dipole- induced dipole	
Induced dipole-induced dipole	Weakest

ION-DIOPLE

As we saw before, many molecules have a permanent dipole, they are polar molecules. Water is one such molecule with the more electronegative oxygen and the less electronegative hydrogen, so water is like a little dipole with partially positive and partially negative areas.

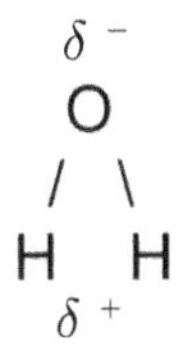

$$\delta^-$$
$$O$$
$$/ \ \backslash$$
$$H \quad H$$
$$\delta^+$$

Ions attract the unlike charge. So for NaCl it ionizes (forms ions) in water giving

$$NaCl \rightarrow Na^+ + Cl^-$$

The Cl^- attracts the hydrogen-rich partially electron poor region actually fitting about six waters about each chloride ion. The Na^+ attracts the oxygen end again fitting about six water molecules about it. The individual binding energies between the ions and water are not great but the total allows water to dissolve many ionic compounds such as NaCl and many organic molecules such as sugars and alcohols, often though hydrogen bonding which is described in the next section.

DIPOLE-DIPOLE

The most important dipole-dipole secondary bond is the **hydrogen bond** where molecules with bonded hydrogen atoms are attached to highly electronegative elements such as O and N. The hydrogen bond is responsible for allowing alcohols, ROH, to dissolve in water HOH. The hydrogen atoms on both the alcohols and water are attached to the highly electronegative oxygen allowing formation of the hydrogen bond between the two oxygen atoms as follows:

R-O-H ------O-H
                    |
                    H

Hydrogen bonding is the reason that water is a liquid at room temperature and not a gas. Compare NH_3 which is a gas, with H_2O and you see the importance such hydrogen bonding. The hydrogen bonding in water is stronger than for ammonia because O is more electronegative than N. Then look at ethane, CH_3CH_3 which is more massive than water but still a gas.

Hydrogen bonding is also important in holding together in precise arrangements protein and nucleic acid polymer chains.

DIPOLE-INDUCED DIPOLE

Dipole-induced dipole bonding is the interaction between polar molecules and non-polar molecules. For instance, it allows the solubility (not high) of oxygen in water. This limited solubility is sufficient to allow fish to "breath oxygen" under water and for plants to survive under water. Water is the dipole that induces (causes) the formation of a temporary dipole in the non-polar oxygen molecule.

INDUCED DIPOLE-INDUCED DIPOLE

Induced dipole-induced dipole bonding is of low energy and result because of very short-lived, temporary attractions. They are also referred to as dispersion forces or dispersion bonding forces or London dispersion forces. All materials have such secondary forces that allow some attraction between them. These forces are about 8 kJ/mol in magnitude per dispersion interaction. These forces are additive. For instance, there is only one dispersion force interaction between methane, CH_4, molecules so methane is a gas under room conditions. Yet octane, C_8H_{18}, which is burned in our cars as fuel, has 8 dispersion interactions between octane molecules and is a liquid. Polyethylene, which is composed of hundreds to thousands of methylene, CH_2, units is a solid because each methylene, CH_2, unit attracts with dispersion attractions, another methylene unit and there are hundreds to thousands of such attractions within each chain. Weight also plays an important part in this trend.

SOLUTIONS

Solutions contain a **solvent** (one or more dissolving materials) and a **solute**(s) (material(s) that is dissolved). Thus, for a salt water solution the solvent is water and the solute is NaCl. We can have **saturated** solutions where all of the solute that can be dissolved is dissolved, and **unsaturated** solutions where less than the maximum amount is dissolved. How can you make a saturated solution? We also have super saturated solutions where more of the solute than is normally soluble in a solution is soluble in it.

There are two main factors that are involved in solubility or mixing. One of these factors is energy. The second factor is described in terms of order or disorder.

"Like-likes-like best of all" is a description that is useful in science. It is true of solubility and mixing and involves the energy term. Thus, water-likes-water best of all and is infinitely soluble in itself. Hexane-likes-hexane best of all and is infinitely soluble in itself. Hexane and water are not soluble in one another because hexane is nonpolar and water is polar, thus they are not "like-one-another." In solubility, and for all mixing, the energy term is always unfavorable when mixing or solubility occurs. But, it is the increase in disorder that allows mixing and solubility to occur. Nature naturally goes from order to disorder. Simply watch your room. You make the beds and hang up the towels and after some time it becomes disordered and you have to "reorder" it again. As seen below the amount of change in randomness or disorder is great when pure materials such as water and H_3C-OH, methanol or methyl alcohol, is changed from the ordered pure materials to the disordered mixture.

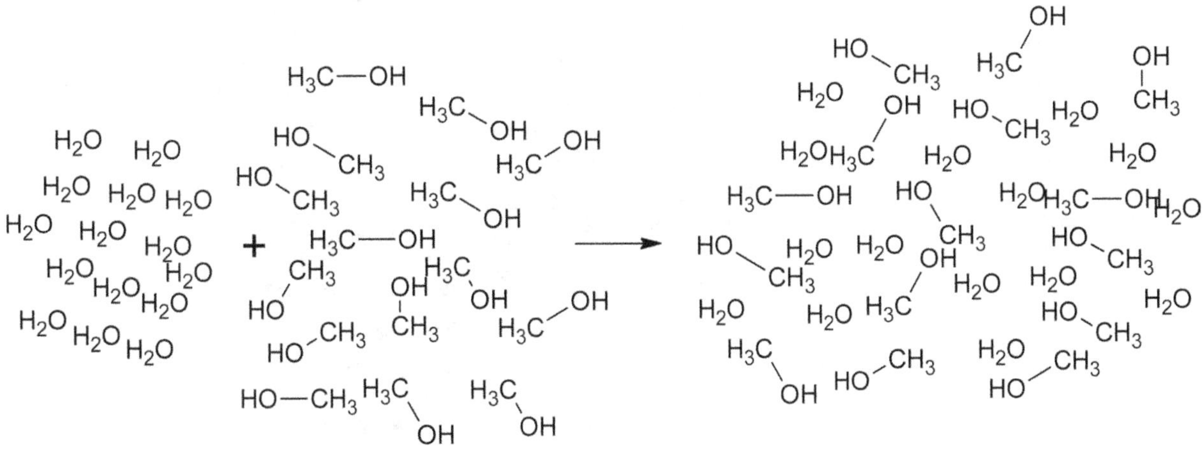

Figure 7.1 *Illustration showing the increase in randomness when mixing occurs.*

Thus, the energy term for mixing and dissolving (solution) is always against mixing and dissolving occurring, but the order/disorder factor always favors mixing and dissolving. The intent is to minimize the energy term through use of solvents and solutes that are alike in their electronic properties if solution and mixing are to occur making use of the "like-likes-like-best-of-all" concept.

In predicting which compounds will dissolve in which solvents we use the concept that like-molecules are more apt to dissolve one another and unlike molecules are less apt to dissolve one another. Thus, we will find that alcohols with R-OH functional groups and sugars that also have R-OH groups are likely to be soluble in water that also has polar OH groups that can hydrogen bond with the sugars and alcohols. Ketones that do not have OH groups but do have polar groups called carbonyls, R = O, can also form hydrogen bonds with water and so are often found to be soluble in water. Salts such as NaCl are also apt to be soluble in water because they are ionic. Hydrocarbons are not polar and not soluble in water.

Counter, non-polar materials are often soluble in one another. Thus hydrocarbons are generally soluble in non-polar solvents, often hydrocarbons themselves. Benzene and hexane are both hydrocarbons and non-polar and they are soluble in one another. Turpentine and gasoline are soluble in one another since both are non-polar.

In general, solubility of **solids** increases with increase in temperature since there is more energy available to cause dissociation of the like molecules. Remember that solubility increases the randomness (an overall driving force in nature) and decreases the number of highly-like "pools" of like molecules.

For gases, the solubility of gases **decreases** with increase in temperature since the volatility of the gases is greatly increased. Pour hot soda into an empty glass and repeat it with a glass filled with ice. Which gives the most fizz? Further, gas solubility increases with increased pressure. That is how the fizz, dissolved CO_2, is added to soft drinks, sodas.

How does soap work?

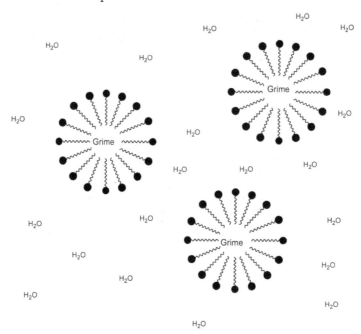

Figure 7.2 *Micelle formation in soap.*

Much grime is non-polar, organic in nature and this is attracted by the non-polar part of the soap micelles. The ionic stains such as blue copper sulfate, the Cu^{+2} ion is captured by the polar side of the soap micelles and removed. The micelles are formed because again of the like-liking-like best so the organic portions bundle together with the polar sides pointing towards the polar water molecules.

Detergents are synthetic soaps. Most have a sulfonate, $-SO_3^{-1}$ end that acts the same as the $-COO^{-1}$ end and the aliphatic end that acts similar to the fatty acid portion of "old" soap. Multivalent (What are they?) cations are especially well chelated by these detergents so they will precipitate the detergents not allowing them to do their job. These multivalent cations are in what is called "**hard**" water and turns "**soft**" water into the hard water by their presence. Water-softer tanks, beds, filters preferentially remove these multivalent cations such as Ca^{+2} and $Fe^{+2, +3}$ making the hard water soft. These water-softer units can be thrown out after they are used up or **recharged** by addition of concentrated solutions of common table salt, NaCl.

MOLE & FORMULA WEIGHT

A **formula weight** is simply the atomic weights of the individual atoms of an element or compound. For covalent compounds the formula weight is also the molecular weight. For water, H_2O, the formula weight is calculated as follows:

2H atoms at 1 amu each = 2 and for 1O atom at 16 amu each = 16 and the total is 18 amu or for the gram formula weight, which is simply the formula weight in grams, it is 18 grams.

The formula weight for a sugar with the formula of $C_6H_{12}O_6$ is calculated as follows:

6C at 12 amu each = 72 amu, plus 12H at 1 amu each = 12 amu, and 6O at 16 amu each = 96 giving a total of 180 amu or 180 grams.

For sodium hydroxide, NaOH it is 1 Na at 23 amu each = 23 amu, plus 1O at 16 amu = 16 amu, and 1O at 1 amu each = 1 amu for a total of 40 amu or 40 grams.

Avogadro's number is the number of individual units in one formula weight of an element or compound. It is 602,000,000,000,000,000,000,000 = 6.02×10^{23} greater than the grains of sand in all the oceans on Earth, greater than all the stars in the sky. Thus, one mole of water is 18 grams and within this 18 grams is 6×10^{23} water molecules, or one Avogadro's number of water molecules. One Avogadro's number of units is called a gram **mole** or simply mole.

Thus, a gram formula weight for a compound or element is called a mole and has one Avogadro's number of formula units in it. So as we calculate the formula weight of water to be 18, this value can have several units attached to it. The formula weight of water is 18, 18 grams, or 18 grams/mole.

In fact the **number of moles is the weight of a material divided by its formula or molecular weight** so for water 18 grams is how many moles? The number of moles = weight of material/gram formula weight of # mol = wt/gfw = 18 g/18 g/mol = 1 mole or 1 mol.

36 grams of water is ____ moles. # mol = 36 g/18 g/mol = 2 mol. This two moles has _____ water molecules.

The **number of units**, here water molecules, is equal to the **# moles times Avogadro's number**

2 moles $\times$ 6 $\times$ 10^{23} water molecules/mol = 12 $\times$ 10^{23} water molecules = 1.2×10^{24} water molecules.

There are two formulas we need to remember from this. First,

Number of moles = Weight/Formula weight and

Number of molecules or formula units = number of moles times Avogadro's number.

MOLARITY

The concentration of a solution is the amount of solute in a solution. This can be given in a number of ways. It can be given in grams per some volume or teaspoons per glass, or … A more concentrated solution will contain more solute in a given amount of solution than a less concentrated solution.

In science, the most common unit of solution concentration is **molarity, M.**
M = number of moles of solute/liters of solution = # moles/Volume (in liters)

This is another formula we need to remember. We also need to be able to use it. Following are some problems we should be able to work.

Q. What is the molarity if 20 grams of NaOH is dissolved to give 1 liter of solution?

A. Gfw for NaOH is 23 (for sodium) + 16 (for oxygen) + 1 (for hydrogen) = 40 g/mol.
So, 20 grams of NaOH is

# mol = wt/gfw = 20 g/40 g/mol = 0.5 mol.
M = # mol/V(in liters) = 0.5 mol/1 L = 0.5 or 0.5 M or 0.5 mol/L

Q. What is the molarity of solution that has 3 moles of sodium chloride dissolved to make one liter of solution?

A. M = # moles/V in liters = 3 moles/1 liter = 3 M

Q. What is the molarity of a solution that has 6 moles of sugar dissolved to make 2 liters of solution?

A. M = # moles/V in liters = 6 moles/2 liters = 3 M

Q. What is the molarity of a solution that has 4 moles of sodium hydroxide dissolved to make 250 mL of solution.

Note: when ever you run across a volume in milliliters, mL, you need to divide it by 1,000 to give you liters. Thus, 250/1,000 = 0.25 L.

A. M = # moles/V in liters = 4 moles/0.25L = 16 M.

Q. How many liters of 2 M sodium chloride solution contains 4 moles of sodium chloride?

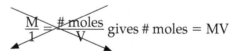 gives # moles = MV

A. Note: we need to rearrange M + # moles/V as above
so that V = # moles/M = 4 moles/2 molar = 2 liters. This is another relationship we need to know-

#moles = MV.

Q. How many moles of sugar are contained in 500 mL solution that is 3 molar?

A. Note: Again, we need to rearrange M = # moles/V so that # moles = M × V = 3 M × 0.5 L = 1.5 moles. We also converted 500 mL to 0.5 L.

More about formula weight and moles in Section 9.

Water

Water is one of the most important compounds we know of. We are largely composed of water, roughly 80%. Much of the surface of the earth is covered by water. Most of the food we eat contains mainly water. Etc. Water is essential to our lives. Thus, it is important to understand water and some of its properties.

Water is one of the very few materials whose liquid form is denser than its solid form.

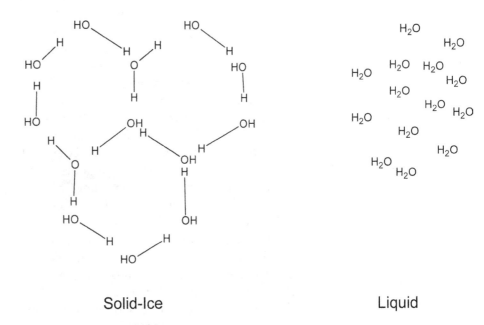

Solid-Ice   Liquid

Figure 8.1 *Representative structure of solid and liquid water.*

Freezing and melting are **equilibrium processes**. Look at what happens to individual ice cubes after they are placed in a drink. (What happens? How is this evidence that freezing and melting is an equilibrium process?)

In a room that is warmer than the freezing point of water, eventually all of the ice/liquid will become liquid. Heat from the room melts the ice. The presence of impurities such as NaCl disrupts the formation of the solid hexagons by secondary bonding of the water molecules to the sodium and chloride ions, thus lowering the freezing point of water. That is why salt is added in the middle states to help keep streets from freezing. (Why is salt not used in the upper states? What are the pros and cons of using salt?)

One of the **Laws of Thermodynamics** is that "heat flows from high to low." Another Law of Thermodynamics is that "things go from bad to worse." What do these statements mean in a practical sense? The statement that heat flows from high to low is one description of the **First Law of Thermodynamics**. In practical terms it says that if you hold an ice cube then heat flows from you to the colder ice cube eventually melting it. The statement that things go from bad to worse is related to the saying that things go from order to disorder. Both are statements of the **Second Law of Thermodynamics**. Thus, there is a tendency for mixing since the pure unmixed material, such as common table salt and sugar, and water itself are in a somewhat ordered state. When we mix sugar with water or salt with water the extent of order had decreased, that is, there is an increase in the disorder of the system. This helps explain why many materials are soluble in water.

As the temperature of ice water increases, the vibrations increase working against formation of the hexagons composing the solid water.

Water is most dense at about 4°C. Between 0 and 4°C the decrease in volume caused by collapsing ice crystals is greater than the increase in volume cause by the faster-moving water molecules. At about 4°C expansion overrides contraction because most of the ice crystals have collapsed. Thus, cooling water when it reaches about 4°C moves to the bottom of the pool, lake, river and it remains a liquid while above it there is a pool of liquid in equilibrium with the ice and finally ice forms. The movement of the 4°C layer causes vertical currents to flow resulting in cycling (upwelling) of materials at the bottom, causing a mixing of these materials.

Water surfaces tend to cling together through hydrogen bonding so that you can "float" a paper clip on water. This tendency to cling together causes what is called **surface tension**. Like-likes-like best is occurring again as the water molecules like one another best so bind together. It also acts to allow water edges to climb polar glass and be caused to go down in a Styrofoam or other plastic non- or less-polar material such as a plastic straw. Try it. Surface tension also accounts for the spherical shape of liquid drops. Remember that the most compact geometry is spherical. The tendency to form spherical drops occurs for all liquids and not just water.

These attractive forces for glass and other polar materials results in what is called capillary action where water is drawn up further in a narrow glass tube. The forces that hold the water molecules together are called cohesive forces and those that draw the water up the sides of the glass, adhesive forces. Eventually, the distance between the sides of the small glass capillary becomes small enough so that both adhesive and cohesive forces tend to move the water level even higher.

Just as freezing and melting are equilibrium events, so also is evaporation and condensation. Except here, the gas phase has the molecules far away from one another so that many water molecules escape, but some do return. But, the net effect is evaporation, even from snow, of the water molecules, many going through the liquid stage, but not all with some going directly from the solid to the gas phase (**sublimation**). When we sweat, the sweat is composed of water molecules that are higher energy (higher temperature) so they evaporate leaving behind the less energetic water molecules resulting in a cooling effect. As wind passes by us, more water molecules are swept away without opportunity to return, so there is a faster rate of evaporation and cooling. The rate of evaporation increases as temperature increases until at the boiling point, most of the water molecules have sufficient energy to escape the liquid becoming gaseous.

As noted before, it takes energy going from ice → liquid → gas and energy is given off going from gas → liquid → solid.

The water vapor in our atmosphere gives off lots of energy as it becomes rain. A hurricane gains a lot of energy from vapor condensing into rain.

It takes different amounts of energy to raise the temperature of different materials. For water, it takes 1 calorie (4.18 joules) of energy to raise the temperature of 1 gram of water 1 degree C. The amount of energy needed to heat 1 gram of material one degree C is called the **specific heat or specific heat capacity or heat capacity.** Conductive materials generally have low heat capacities whereas liquids have higher heat capacities. Phase changes also require energy and these energies are often given the name "heat of -----", such as heat of melting, heat of freezing, etc.

Water dissolves polar and ionic compounds. Because the water molecule is composed of the more electronegative oxygen atom and less electronegative hydrogen atoms, it exists as a little molecular dipole with a partially negative or electron rich oxygen end and a partially positive or electron poor end where the two hydrogen atoms reside. As a salt, NaCl, crystal is dropped into water the electron poor hydrogen end works to attract the chloride ions and the electron rich oxygen end works to attract the sodium cations ripping the crystal apart resulting in the salt being dissolved. Even in solution these attractions are at work so each sodium ion will have about 6 waters about it with the oxygen end of water pointed towards it and the chloride ion will also have about 6 water molecules about it with the electron poor partially positive hydrogen end pointed towards the chlorine as shown below.

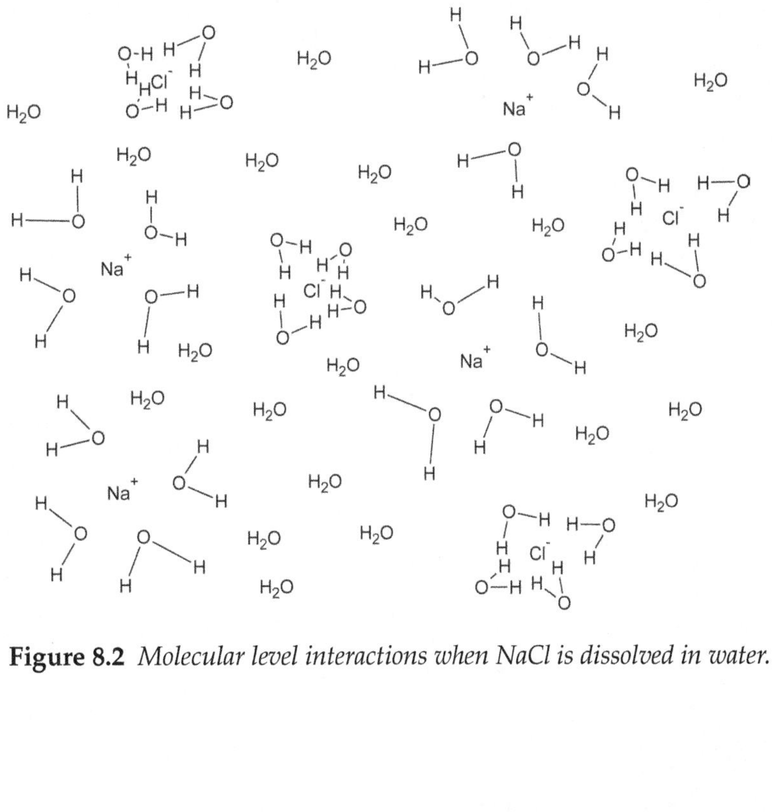

Figure 8.2 *Molecular level interactions when NaCl is dissolved in water.*

Chemical Reactions & Equations

WRITING CHEMICAL EQUATIONS

A chemical equation is the symbolic representation of a chemical reaction utilizing chemical formulas-it is a chemistry "short-hand".

$$A + B \rightarrow C + D$$

is "read" as "the reaction of A with B "goes to"
"gives"
"react to form"
"yields" C and D.

A and B are called the **REACTANTS**, the arrow is read "goes to", "react to form", "yields" or "gives" and C and D are called the **PRODUCTS**.

It is customary to write **BALANCED** equations such that the _**NUMBER**_ and _**KIND**_ of atoms appearing on the RIGHT (or reactant) side of the arrow are EQUAL (in number and kind) to those atoms that appear on the LEFT (or product) side.

COEFFICIENTS (numbers that appear before the formula weight of a material in the equation) are added to BALANCE the equation-make the number and kind of atoms (not compounds) that react be the same in number and kind as appear as products. Thus, it is the ATOMS that are balanced-not molecules, compounds.

(Thus, for the balanced equation $2H_2 + O_2 \rightarrow 2H_2O$ the 2 in front of H_2 and H_2O is a coefficient and says that to have a balanced equation we need 2 H_2 units and 2 H_2O units. There is an understood "1" in front of the O_2 that is not written but we know that it is there. Notice that we can also write this equation by changing the order of hydrogen and oxygen as follows. $O_2 + 2H_2 \rightarrow 2H_2O$. We can also write this going in the opposite direction just as long as the products and reactants are the same. $2H_2O \leftarrow 2H_2 + O_2$.)

Further, the "form" or "phase" of the reactants and products may also be indicated where (g) = gas; (l) = liquid, (s) = solid, and (aq) indicates an aqueous (water) solution.

Thus, for the reaction of diatomic (contains TWO atoms of oxygen) oxygen gas and diatomic (contains TWO atoms of hydrogen) hydrogen gas to form gaseous water we have

$$O_2 + H_2 \rightarrow H_2O$$

as the "unbalanced" equation where

"O_2" and "H_2" are REACTANTS and the "H_2O" is the PRODUCT.

We can "BALANCE" the reaction by placing a "2" in front of "H_2" and in front of "H_2O". Since "O_2" appears in the balanced equation only once, by agreement, we "understand" that a "1" is there and do not place the "1" in the equation.

Thus the "completed" equation (including the phases) is as follows:

$O_{2(g)} + 2H_{2(g)} \rightarrow 2H_2O_{(g)}$ or more typical without the phases as

$$O_2 + 2H_2 \rightarrow 2H_2O$$

Practice "balancing" and writing equations. This is a skill that will be required throughout your chemistry classes-as well as other classes that include chemical reactions.

Before we leave our introduction to balanced reactions, let us compare what a balanced equation is and is not. The balanced equation is

$$2H_2 + O_2 \rightarrow 2H_2O$$

It is not $4H_2 + 2O_2 \rightarrow 4H_2O$ because the prefixes, coefficients, are not present in the smallest whole number value.

It is not $H_2 + 1/2\ O_2 \rightarrow H_2O$ because the coefficients must be whole numbers. So while each of these wrong examples of having the same number of each kind of atom on both sides of the arrow, they are not correct as noted.

Finally, a balanced equation is important because the coefficients tell us how the number of moles and molecules are related to one another. Thus the balanced equation

$$2H_2 + O_2 \rightarrow 2H_2O$$

tells us that two molecules of hydrogen reacts with one molecule of oxygen forming two molecules of water OR two moles of hydrogen reacts with one mole of oxygen to form two moles of water. It DOES NOT tell us that 2 grams of hydrogen reacts with one gram of oxygen to give us two grams of water.

DEFINITIONS

Let us recall some important relationships.

Number of moles = Weight/Formula weight and

Number of molecules or formula units = number of moles times Avogadro's number.

A **FORMULA** is the notation using atomic symbols and appropriate numerical subscripts to convey the relative number of atoms of different elements that make-up the particular compound.

$NaHCO_3$ has one sodium atom, one hydrogen atom, one carbon atom for every three oxygen atoms. Common table salt $NaCl$ has one sodium atoms for every one chloride atom.

MOLECULE- definite group of atoms that are chemically bonded together. Thus, each molecule of water has one oxygen atom and two hydrogen atoms-or three atoms total. This combination of one oxygen and two hydrogen atoms persists until chemically altered. Here, electrons are "shared", not lost as in the case of ionic substances.

MOLECULAR FORMULA- chemical formula that gives the total number of atoms of each element in the molecule. Thus benzene, a simple organic solvent, has six carbon atoms and six hydrogen atoms in EACH molecule of benzene.

Ethanol has two carbons, six hydrogen atoms and one oxygen atom for EACH molecule.

STRUCTURAL FORMULA- is a representation of the shape of the molecule or the way the atoms are arranged to form a molecule. Structural Formulas can be simple representations or more complex "MOLECULAR" models such as space-filling and ball-and-stick models.

In actuality, the formula weight applies to both ionic and covalent compounds whereas molecular weight applies to only covalently bonded compounds.

MOLECULAR WEIGHT- sum of the atomic weights of all atoms in a covalently bonded molecule of substance

Benzene- C_6H_6 (covalent bonded)= 6×12 amu/carbon + 6×1 amu/ hydrogen= 78 amu

Acetone- CH_3COCH_3 (covalent bonded) = 3×12 amu/carbon + 6×1 amu/hydrogen + 1×16 amu/oxygen = 58 amu

Dinitrogen tetraoxide- N_2O_4 (covalent bonded) = 2×14 amu/nitrogen + 4×16 amu/oxygen = 92 amu

FORMULA WEIGHT- sum of the atomic weights of all the atoms in a formula unit of the compound be it covalent or ionic bonded.

Glass-largely SiO_2 (covalent bonded) = 1×28 amu/silicon + 2×16 amu/oxygen = 60 amu

NaOH (ionic bonded between the Na and OH units) 1×23 amu/sodium + 1×16 amu/oxygen + 1×1 amu/hydrogen = 40 amu

Magnesium hydroxide- $Mg(OH)_2$ (ionic bonded between OH and Mg units)= 1×24.3 amu/magnesium + 2×16 amu/oxygen + 2×1 amu/hydrogen = 58.3 amu

---

MOLE-RELATED PROBLEMS

Remember that **ONE MOLE = FORMULA (OR MOLECULAR) WEIGHT** and that **ONE GRAM MOLE = FORMULA (OR MOLECULAR) WEIGHT** in **GRAMS**.

Q. How many grams of water are in ½ moles of water.

A. We have that # moles = Wt /GFW. We can rearrange this to solve for Wt = # moles times GFW. Thus, Wt = ½ mole times 18 grams/mole = 9 grams.

Q. How many molecules of water are in 9 grams of water?

A. Remember that one gram mole, one gram formula weight and one gram molecular weight have 6×10^{23} units or molecules

Thus, # of molecules = # moles $\times 6 \times 10^{23}$ molecules/mole =

0.5 moles $\times 6 \times 10^{23}$ molecules/mole = 3×10^{23} molecules

Q. What is the weight of one molecule of water.

A. We know that 6×10^{23} molecules weigh 18 grams or that there are 6×10^{23} molecules/gram formula (molecular) weight and for water there is 18 grams/gram formula (molecular) weight-thus

$$\frac{18 \text{ grams/gram molecular weight}}{6 \times 10^{23} \text{ molecules/gram molecular weight}} = 3 \times 10^{-23} \quad \text{grams}$$

We can also set this up as a simple proportion as follows. We remember that one mole weights one GFW and has 6×10^{23} units so

$$\frac{18 \text{ grams}}{X \text{ grams}} = \frac{6 \times 10^{23} \text{ water molecules}}{1 \text{ water molecule}}$$

Cross multiplication and solving for X, the weight of one water molecule, gives

$$X \text{ grams} = 18 \text{ grams} \times 1 \text{ water molecule}/6 \times 10^{23} \text{ water molecules} = 3 \times 10^{-23} \text{ grams}$$

Q. Given 160 grams of sodium hydroxide, NaOH, how many moles, units and sodium atoms are there.

A. First determine the gram formula weight of NaOH

1×23 amu/sodium atom $+ 1 \times 1$ amu/hydrogen atom $+ 1 \times 16$ amu/oxygen atom $= 40$ amu or 40 grams/mole or 40 grams/6×10^{23} units of NaOH

Moles = mass (weight)/gram formula weight = 160 g/40 g/mole = 4 moles

Units of NaOH = 4 moles $\times 6 \times 10^{23}$ NaOH units/mole $= 24 \times 10^{23}$ NaOH units $= 2.4 \times 10^{24}$ NaOH units

The number of atoms of sodium is the same as the number of units of NaOH since each NaOH units contains one sodium atom.

MASS PERCENTAGES

Mass percentages from the formula are calculated from

% Element = (mass of particular element/total mass) × 100

Q. What is the % of H, O and Na in NaOH (by mass, not number)?

A. Determine the formula weight. 1×1 amu/hydrogen $+ 1 \times 16$ amu/oxygen $+ 1 \times 23$ amu/sodium $= 40$ amu.

% H = $(1/40) \times 100 = 2.5$ % hydrogen

% O = $(16/40) \times 100 = 40$ % oxygen

%Na = $(23/40) \times 100 = 57.5$ % sodium

Sum total of $2.5 + 40 + 57.5 = 100$ %

Q. What is the % carbon & hydrogen in benzene-C_6H_6

A. Determine the molecular weight. 6×12 amu/carbon $+ 6 \times 1$ amu/hydrogen $= 78$ amu.

% C = $(72/78) \times 100 = 92\%$

% H = $(6/78) \times 100 = 8\%$

Sum total is 100 %.

STOICHIOMETRY: QUANTITATIVE RELATIONSHIPS IN CHEMICAL REACTIONS

Because many of the problems have several steps to them it is often wise to develop a strategy to solve the problem. One type of strategy is to develop so-called "road maps" where the individual steps from start to finish are identified. Following is such a road map for creating the weight that can be obtained in a reaction when a specific weight of product is given. This "road map" can also give the amount of reactant needed to make a given amount of product; amount of reactant needed to react with another amount of reactant; etc. Thus it is a useful road map for many types of quantitative problems involving chemical reactions. Please remember that the key to successfully employing this approach is a **balanced** equation. The coefficients to the balanced equation connect the necessary molar amounts within the equation.

Road Map
　　Weight → Moles → Balanced Equation → Moles → Weight

This is a <u>reversible</u> road map-that is we can go in either direction.

Balanced reactions form the basis for determining the quantitative relationships in chemical reactions. Thus, for the reaction of

$$2H_2 + O_2 \rightarrow 2H_2O$$

we know the relationships between all of the reactants. Thus, we know that
　　2 moles of hydrogen react with one mole of oxygen giving 2 moles of water

30 molecules	react with 15 molecules	giving 30 molecules
2.6 moles	react with 1.3 moles	giving 2.6 moles
but **NOT**		
3 GRAMS	react with 1.5 GRAMS	giving 3 GRAMS

in other words-the ratio of reactants and products is

$$2 \text{ to } 1 \rightarrow 2$$

using as the "counting factor" **the coefficients**.

We are able to associate masses through remembering that

One mole = one gram formula weight or one molecular weight.

There are different approaches to telling how many molecules or moles is needed using a balanced equation given the moles of one reactant. Following is one called the proportion approach.

　Q. We have

$$2H_2 + O_2 \rightarrow 2H_2O$$

Given 5 moles of oxygen, how many moles of water can be made?

　A. The mole relationship between oxygen and water in the <u>balanced</u> equation is $1O_2 \rightarrow 2\ H_2O$. We than can set up the proportion as follows

$$\frac{1O_2}{5} = \frac{2H_2O}{X} \quad \text{And solving for } X = 10.$$

Watch, the top half of the proportion comes from the coefficients of the balanced equation for the chemicals involved and the bottom two values comes from the problem.

Q. For the Haber process $N_2 + 3H_2 \rightarrow 2NH_3$.
How many moles of hydrogen are needed to produce 5 moles of ammonia?

A. Again, set up the proportion $\dfrac{3H_2}{X} = \dfrac{2NH_3}{5}$

Solving for $X = 15/2 = 7.5$ moles of hydrogen are needed.

Q. How many grams of ammonia are produced from 12 moles of nitrogen.

A. The proportion is then $\dfrac{1N_2}{12} = \dfrac{2NH_3}{X}$

and $X = 24$ moles of ammonia
Grams of ammonia = 24 moles $\times$ 17 grams/mole = 408 grams
This proportion approach is also good for solving other kinds of problems.

Q. If 4 grams of a compound contains 1.8×10^{23} repeat units, then one mole weights how many grams.

A. We set up the proportion from what is given and what we know.

$$\frac{4 \text{ grams}}{X \text{ grams}} = \frac{1.8 \times 10^{23}}{6 \times 10^{23}} \quad \text{And } X = 13.3 \text{ grams}$$

Q. How many moles of iron atoms are in 6.00 grams of iron?

A. You could remember that the number of moles = weight/g formula weight or

$$\frac{6 \text{ grams}}{56 \text{ grams}} = \frac{X \text{ moles}}{1 \text{ mole}} \quad \text{And } X = 0.107 \text{ moles}$$

We will practice the proportion method using the Haber process. The Haber process for the synthesis of ammonia is one of the most important synthetic chemical processes we have. Much of the nitrogen we use for fertilizer is "fixed" (put into usable form) through the Haber process.

$$N_2 + 3H_2 \rightarrow 2NH_3$$

Q. How many molecules of ammonium can we make from 12 molecules of nitrogen?

A. We must use a BALANCED equation. Using the BALANCED equation we relate the coefficients letting our unknown be represented by "X".

$1N_2/12$ molecules of $N_2 = 2NH_3/X$ molecules NH_3

Solving for X gives

X molecules of $NH_3 = 2NH_3$ times 12 molecules of $N_2/1N_2 = 24$ molecules of NH_3

Q. How many moles of ammonium can we make from 6 moles of hydrogen?

A. Again, using a BALANCED equation and letting "X" be the unknown number of ammonia that can be made we again set up the proportion as follows.

$3H_2/6$ moles of $H_2 = 2NH_3/X$ moles of NH_3

Again, solving for "X" we get

X moles of $NH_3 = 6$ moles H_2 times $2NH_3/3H_2 = 4$ moles of NH_3

Q. What weight in grams of nitrogen is necessary to make 10 grams of ammonia?

A. From the BALANCED equation we know that one mole of nitrogen gives us two moles of ammonia.

Q. First, let us calculate the number of moles of ammonia in 10 grams of ammonia.

A. The molecular weight (or number of grams per mole) of ammonia is

1×14 amu/nitrogen $+ 3 \times 1$ amu/hydrogen $= 17$ amu or 17 grams/mole

# of moles of ammonia is weight of ammonium/molecular weight of ammonia

10 grams/17 grams/mole $= 0.59$ moles.

Next, let us remember that for every two moles of ammonia we have one mole of nitrogen so the (mole) ratio of ammonia to nitrogen is 2:1. Thus, the number of moles of nitrogen necessary to make 0.59 moles of ammonia is

$$0.59/2 = \text{about } 0.295 \text{ moles.}$$

Now we can calculate the number of grams of nitrogen that is in 0.295 moles as follows: 28 grams/mole $\times$ 0.295 mole $= 8.3$ grams of nitrogen is needed to make 10 grams of ammonia.

REACTION RATES

Reaction rates tell about the speed of reactions; they tell us how fast reactants are used up and products are formed. Reaction rates increase with increase in temperature. For a reaction to occur there must be sufficient energy. The energy barrier needed to be overcome, the barrier to getting the reactants to change into products, is called the **activation energy** or **energy of activation**. Thus, to get H_2 and O_2 to react forming H_2O sufficient energy must be available to push them together allowing the H-H and O-O bonds to break and reform to give H-O-H bonds. **Reaction rate increases as temperature increases** since increased temperature means that more of the reactants will have sufficient energy to get over the activation energy barrier. Conversely, reaction rate decreases as temperature decreases. This is another example of a direct relationship.

To react the molecules must come into contact, often 10^{10} times or more and they must be in the right geometry. Catalysts generally place molecules in the right geometry so that this hurdle is lowered acting to lower the overall activation energy. Since molecules must come into contact to react, **reaction rate is increased as the concentration of reactants increases**.

Reactions are either net **exothermic**, giving off energy like the burning of natural gases and petroleum products, or **endothermic**, taking in a net amount of energy (cold packs). Below are two "reaction profiles." The one on the left is for an endothermic reaction and the one on the right is for an exothermic reaction. The heat of reaction which tells if it is exothermic or endothermic is the potential energy difference between the reactants and products. If the potential energy for the products is above that of the reactants, then the reaction is endothermic; conversely, if the potential energy for the products is below that of the reactants, then the reaction is exothermic and a net amount of energy is given off.

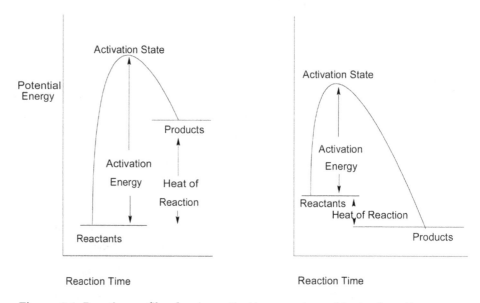

Figure 9.1 *Reaction profiles showing activation energies and heats of reaction.*

The energy difference between the reactants and the activation state is called the **activation energy** or **energy of activation**. The reaction rate or speed of a reaction is related to the activation energy. In general, if the activation energy is relatively low or small, the reaction will be fast or rapid; conversely, if the activation energy is relatively high or great, the reaction will be slow. The relationship is called an exponential relationship so that small activation energy differences are reflected in large changes in the rate.

The rate of a reaction is related to the amount of energy or heat available. As the energy available to run a reaction becomes greater, more molecules will have the necessary energy to overcome the activation energy and the faster the reaction. Again, the relationship between reaction rate and temperature is exponential so that relatively small temperature variations will greatly influence the rate.

Enzymes are proteins that are natural catalysts. They lower the energy of activation through assuring the correct geometry (orientation) as well as holding the reactants in the general vicinity of one another so that they do not have to "find" one another. These catalysts can have a phenomenal affect on the reaction rate. One reaction takes about a billion years to occur but in the presence of the correct catalysts occurs in picoseconds, an increase in about 10^{17}.

Acids and Bases

THEORIES OF ACIDS AND BASES

There are several general approaches to acids and bases. There are two definitions we will use to define acids and bases on a molecular level. These are the Bronsted-Lory and Arrhenius definitions for acids and bases. For the **Bronsted-Lory** definition

Acid = proton (hydrogen ion; hydronium ion) donator and a
Base = proton acceptor of the proton.

$$HCl + H_2O \rightarrow Cl^{-1} + H_3O^{+1}$$
Acid + Base

$$HCl + NaOH \rightarrow NaCl + H_2O$$
Acid + Base $\rightarrow$ Salt + Water

$$HCl + NH_3 \rightarrow NH_4Cl \text{ or}$$
$$HCl + NH_4OH \rightarrow NH_4Cl + H_2O$$

For the **Arrhenius** definition an **acid** increases the concentration of the H^{+1} (H_3O^{+1}) and a **base** increases the concentration of the OH^{-1} (hydroxide) ion in aqueous (water-based) solutions. Note that the only difference between H^{+1} and H_3O^{+1} is the presence of a single water molecule in the second formula. The H_3O^{+1} is called a **hydronium ion** whereas the H^{+1} or simply H^+ is called a **proton** (since it is a hydrogen atom minus its lone electron leaving only a proton remaining) or **hydrogen ion**. Above, HCl is an acid since it increases the H_3O^+ concentration whereas sodium hydroxide is a base since it increases the OH^- concentration.

$$NaOH \rightarrow Na^+ + OH^-$$

A **salt** is the product of the reaction between an acid and a base.

$$HCl + NaOH \rightarrow NaCl + H_2O$$

Acid + Base $\rightarrow$ Salt + Water

The reaction between an acid and a base is also referred to as a **neutralization reaction** because the acid (base) neutralizes the base (acid).

Acid/base reactions have as products a salt and water. Thus, please remember that an acid plus a base gives a salt and water as shown above.

Some acids and bases are stronger than others.

ELECTROLYTES

Electrolytes are compounds that supply ions when dissolved in water (forming an aqueous solution) thus causing the solution to conduct electrical current.

Non-electrolytes are compounds that do not produce ions, do not produce conducting solutions.

We use electrolyte strength as a measure of the proportion of an acid or base that provides protons or hydroxide ions. We will call an acid/base strong if it gives a high fraction of protons or hydroxide ions since they form lots of ions and are able to conduct electrical charge. It is then a strong electrolyte.

For instance HI is a strong acid because $HI \rightarrow H^{+1} + I^{-1}$ almost 100 %.

By comparison NH_4OH is a weak base and **weak electrolyte** because while it dissolves only a few ions are formed.

Using the Arrhenius acid/base definition the following are strong acids: HX (where $X = Cl$, Br, and I), HNO_3 and H_2SO_4. Strong bases are I (alkaline metals) and IIA (alkaline earths) hydroxides such as KOH, $LiOH$, $NaOH$, and $Ca(OH)_2$. The major weak base is ammonium hydroxide, NH_4OH. There are many weak acids including phosphoric acid, formic acid, carbonic acid, acetic acid (major component to vinegar), citric acid, etc.

pH SCALE

$$pH = -\log[H_3O^{+1}] = -\log[H^+] \text{ and}$$

$$pOH = -\log[OH^{-1}]$$

$$H^+ + OH^- \leftrightharpoons H_2O \text{ equilibrium}$$

$$K_{eq} = [H^+][OH^-]/[H_2O] \text{ multiplying both sides by } [H_2O] \text{ gives}$$

$$K_{eq}[H_2O] = K_{water} = [H^+][OH^-] = 10^{-14}$$

taking the negative log of both sides gives

$$14 = -\text{Log} [H^+] - \log [OH^-] \text{ and defining } pH = -\text{Log} [H^+] \text{ and}$$

$$pOH = -\log [OH^-] \text{ and}$$

$$pH + pOH = 14$$

This results in the so-called pH scale that ranges from 0 to 14 and where neutral is a pH of 7. Solutions with pH values below 7 (such as 2.1 and 6.2) are acidic and those above 7 (like 8.4 and 12.2) are said to be basic.

Q. What is the pH of lemon juice if $[H^+] = 0.0032$? $[H^+] = 3.2 \times 10^{-3}$

A. $pH = -\text{Log} [H^+] = -\text{Log } 3.2 - \text{Log } 10^{-3} = -\{0.51 - 3\} = 2.49$

Q. What is the pH of a HNO_3 solution that is 0.21 M? Nitric acid is a strong acid so the $[H^+] = 0.21 = 2.1 \times 10^{-1}$.

A. $pH = -Log\,[H^+] = -Log\,.21 - Log\,10^{-1} = -\{0.32 - 1\} = 0.68$ M

Q. What is the pH of vinegar is the $[H^+] = 0.0016$? $[H^+] = 1.6 \times 10^{-3}$

A. $pH = -Log\,[H^+] = -Log\,1.6 - Log\,10^{-3} = -[0.20 - 3] = 2.80$

Q. What is the $[H^+]$ if the pH = 3.12?

A. Remember that $[H^+] = 10^{-pH} = 10^{-3.12} = 7.6 \times 10^{-4}$ M

Q. What is the pH of sea water if $[H^+] = 8.3$?

A. $[H^+] = 10^{-pH} = 10^{-8.3} = 5.0 \times 10^{-9}$ M

If an acidic (acid) solution contains more protons than hydroxide ions then its pH is less than 7; a basic (base) solution contains more hydroxide ions than protons and its pH is greater than 7. A neutral solution contains the same concentration of protons and hydroxide ions. Its pH is 7.

Below is a brief description of the pH scale and some of the materials that correspond to the particular pH.

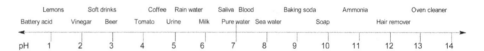

Figure 10.1 *pH range and materials that correspond to particular pHs.*

ACID RAIN

Rainwater is acidic. Why? There are three main sources of acid rain. All three are both man-made and natural.

One man-made source is the coals and petroleum stocks we burn for fuel. Coal and the petrochemicals have come from the decay of plants and animals that contained proteins and nucleic acids that have sulfur and nitrogen in them. These form nitrogen oxides and sulfur oxides. There are a variety of sulfur and nitrogen oxides that are formed from the production of energy from fossil fuels.

The main sulfur oxides include sulfur dioxide and sulfur trioxide. Both of these react with atmospheric water forming acids.

$$SO_3 + H_2O \rightarrow H_2SO_4 \text{ (strong acid)}$$

$$SO_2 + H_2O \rightarrow H_2SO_3 \text{ (weak acid)}$$

Further the sulfur dioxide can react with oxygen forming sulfur trioxide the direct precursor to sulfuric acid.

$$SO_2 + O_2 \rightarrow SO_3$$

The major nitrogen oxides similarly form nitric acid and nitrous acid.

$$NO_2 + H_2O \rightarrow HNO_3 \text{ (strong acid)}$$

As we have already noted, the main products from burning hydrocarbons such as the petroleum feedstocks as fuel and materials with carbon, hydrogen and oxygen such as trees and tree derivatives of paper and wood, are carbon dioxide and water. Further, our respiration creates carbon dioxide. Thus, there are ample sources of carbon dioxide. Carbon dioxide reacts with water forming carbonic acid, a weak acid.

$$CO_2 + H_2O \rightarrow H_2CO_3 \text{ (carbonic acid)}$$

All of these, and other acids, are formed in the atmosphere and come down when it rains- thus the term "acid rain." Thus, our rain, lakes and rivers are somewhat acidic because of this acid rain. Also, most items, including our skin, are somewhat degraded by acid and over an extended period are destroyed by the acid rain. Many of the old tombstones, monuments, and building are composed of limestone, $CaCO_3$. These structures show the ravages of acid rain. While limestone is not appreciably soluble in water, it is more rapidly attacked by acid eventually forming water soluble hydrogen carbonate ion, effecting leaving the original limestone structure with some of the calcium carbonate dissolved away.

$$CaCO_3 + H^{+1} \rightarrow Ca^{+2} + HCO_3^{-1}$$

By comparison, the ocean is basic because of so-called basic salts such as metal carbonates and phosphates that are common in the ocean. There is a lot of limestone in the ocean and as already noted; it is very slightly soluble forming the carbonate and calcium ions.

$$CaCO_3 \rightarrow Ca^{+2} + CO_3^{-2}$$

Because the carbonate ion is the anion from the weak acid carbonic acid, it takes a proton from water resulting in the formation of the hydroxide ion that finally results in the ocean being a little basic.

$$CO_3^{-2} + H_2O \rightarrow HCO_3^{-1} + OH^{-1}$$

Buffer solutions resist pH change. Thus, the addition of sodium acetate to HCl will increase the pH and resist further change.

$$HCl + H_3CCOONa \rightarrow H_3CCOOH + NaCl$$

Acetic acid, a weak acid, forms because acetic acid is a weak acid and takes the proton increasing the pH.

If acetic acid is added to NaOH a similar thing occurs with similar consequences of the pH being driven towards 7.

$$NaOH + H_3CCOOH \rightarrow H_3CCOONa + H_2O$$

Solutions containing the salt of weak acid or base then moderate pH change and are called buffers because of this moderating action.

Oxidation and Reduction (Redox)

Oxidation-reduction or REDOX reactions involve an EXCHANGE of ELECTRONS. **Where there is oxidation there must also be reduction**.

OXIDATION NUMBERS

We assign oxidation numbers according to some rules that are related to the chemical tendencies and placement within the periodic chart of the specific elements. These rules allow us to assign what is called an OXIDATION NUMBER to atoms within a compound. These rules are as follows:

1. The oxidation number of an element is zero. Examples: Fe, O_2, Al, Xe, Cl_2 all have an oxidation number of zero.

2. For monoatomic ions, the oxidation number is the charge on the ion. Thus Ca^{+2} has an oxidation number of plus two. For Cl^{-1} the oxidation number is minus or negative one. Examples: $Na^+ = 1$, $Ba^{+2} = 2$, $Cl^{-1} = -1$, $Fe^{+2} = 2$, $H^+ = 1$, $O^{-2} = -2$

3. Polyatomic ions, such as the hydroxyl radical, and the nitrate radical have, as a radical, their assigned charges-thus for the hydroxide it is a minus one. Examples: nitrate- the grouping NO_3^{-1} has a net -1 for the group; the grouping sulfate, SO_4^{-2} has a net -2 charge for the sulfate grouping.

4. **(a)** Group I A (alkaline metals) and II A (alkaline earths) elements in a compound are $+1$ and $+2$. Thus the oxidation number of Na, K, Li is $+1$; Ca, Sr, Ba is $+2$.

   (b) Hydrogen can be either $+1$ or -1 depending on what it is combined with. If it is with a metal such as in NaH it is a -1 and for non-metals like in HCl and CH_4 it is a $+1$.

   (c) Oxygen is generally a -2 except in peroxides where it is -1.

   (d) Halogens are normally -1 unless combined with another non-metal where it may be something else.

5. The sum of the oxidation numbers in a neutral compound is zero. For a charged radical or ion, the sum of the oxidation numbers will be the charge associated with the radical (as in 3 above)

   There is a "pecking order" to these rules so that if there is a conflict, then the rule with the lowest numbering takes precedence.

Table 11.1 *Summary of characteristics of oxidation and reduction.*

OXIDATION	REDUCTION
Increased oxidation number	**Decreased** oxidation number
Loss in electrons	**Gain** in electrons
Called **reducing agent**	Called **oxidizing agent**
But	But
It is oxidized	It is reduced

Note that the terms under "oxidation" are the opposite of those under "reduction" so that they complement one another. Remember, that the processes of oxidation and reduction are tied to one another as are the definitions related to them. Thus, oxidation is an **increase** in oxidation number while reduction is a **loss** in oxidation number; oxidation is an **increase** in oxidation number but a **loss** in electrons while reduction is a **loss** in oxidation number but it is a **gain** in electrons; a material that is oxidized causes reduction so is a reducing agent while a material that is reduced causes oxidation so is an oxidizing agent.

In assigning oxidation numbers the compound or grouping can be composed of elements whose oxidation numbers are known. For instance, for NaCl it is known that Na is a plus one and Cl is a negative one. But, in other instances the compound or grouping is composed of elements where one of the members can have several oxidation numbers depending on the other elements present. It is important to recognize those elements that typically have a given oxidation number and those elements that can have different oxidation numbers. Elements that can have variable oxidation numbers include transition metals, sulfur, carbon, phosphorus, and nitrogen. Thus, in looking at the compound CrO_2 we see that is contains a transition metal, Cr, and oxygen whose oxidation number is almost always a minus two. Knowing that CrO_2 is neutral we note that there are two oxygen atoms each with a minus two giving a net minus 4. Since the compound is neutral we ask the question what can be added to a minus 4 to get zero and the answer will be the oxidation number of Cr. The answer is +4 which is then the oxidation number of Cr. While halides such as F, Cl, Br, and I are typically −1, there are instances where the other atoms in the compound are also known and higher on the oxidation number rule chart. Thus, for the compound HBrO we have such a situation. H is a +1, O is a −2, so it is Br whose oxidation number must be determined. In this case, since HBrO is not charged, we have H = +1, O = −2 leaving Br = +1. For HBrO4 we have that H = +1, each O = −2 for a total of −8 so that Br in this compound has an oxidation number of +7.

For practice determine the oxidation number for each element in the following compounds.

Examples $CaCO_3$ Ca = +2, O = −2/each and for three is it a total of −6; therefore C = + 2 − 6 = + 4 = 0

$KMnO_4$ MnO_2

K_2CrO_4 CrO CrO_2 CrO_3 $K_2Cr_2O_7$

H_3PO_4 H_3PO_3 P_4O_{10} P_4O_6

H_2SO_4 H_2SO_3 H_2S SO_2 SO_3

NO NO_2 N_2O_4 HNO_3 HNO_2

$FeCl_2$ $FeCl_3$

$CuCl_2$ Cu_2Cl_2

$CaNaPO_4$ $NaHCO_3$ SO_4^{-2} ClO_4^{-1}

CH_4 CH_3Cl CH_2Cl_2 $CHCl_3$ CCl_4 CO_2 CO

To help recall the definitions remember that the concept of redox comes from the reaction of oxygen with metals such as iron. Thus, we can use the reaction between iron and oxygen to help us remember the definitions. We know that iron is oxidized because it has reacted with oxygen.

$$For\ 2Fe + O_2 \rightarrow 2FeO$$

Iron goes from a 0 to +2 so it is a gain in oxidation number so it is **oxidized**, and it is a **reducing agent** because it "causes" oxygen to be reduced. $Fe \rightarrow Fe^{+2} + 2e^-$ so it loses electrons.

Oxygen goes from an oxidation number of 0 to −2 so it's oxidation number is decreased so it is **reduced**, and it is an **oxidizing agent** because it "causes" iron to be oxidized.

$$O_2 + 4e^- \rightarrow 2O^{-2}\ so\ it\ gains\ electrons.$$

Let us look at another example.

$$Ca + Cl_2 \rightarrow CaCl_2$$

Calcium is oxidized since its oxidation number goes from zero to +2, an increase in its oxidation number. The oxidation half cell is

$$Ca \rightarrow Ca^{+2} + 2e^-$$

so consistent with our knowledge of oxidation we have a gain in oxidation number and loss of electrons. Because as we will shortly see, calcium causes chlorine to be reduced, it is an agent of reduction or a reducing agent.

REDUCTION- is the opposite of OXIDATION and is defined as the LOSS in oxidation number or the GAIN in electrons. The reduction half cell is

$$Cl - Cl + 2e^- \rightarrow 2Cl^-$$

Thus, diatomic chlorine decreases, lowers its oxidation number from zero to minus one per chlorine atom. Consistent with our definitions, chlorine not only decreases its oxidation number but also gains electrons and since it supplies electrons to calcium causing calcium to be oxidized it is called a reducing agent.

Be able to assign oxidation numbers to atoms in a compound and to identify whether oxidation or reduction has occurred and to identify the agents of oxidation and reduction. Be able to identify redox reactions.

BALANCING REDOX REACTIONS

Redox reactions generally cannot be balanced by simple inspection. Many redox reactions are carried out in aqueous solution in the presence of an acid or base. Often we add the parts that are acid or base and the corresponding water after we concentrate on the redox-portion of the reaction-Thus H^+ or OH^- is added along with H_2O.

Two general approaches are often taken in balancing redox reactions.

The first method is called the **half-cell** or **half-reaction** method. The following is designed for a redox reaction occurring in acid. $KMnO_4 + KNO_2 \rightarrow MnO_2 + K NO_3$

1. Divide the unbalanced reaction into an oxidation half-reaction and a reduction half-reaction or half-cell.

$$MnO_4^- \rightarrow MnO_2$$

and

$$NO_2 \rightarrow NO_3$$

For each half-reaction do the following.

2. Balance the nonhydrogen and nonoxygen atoms in each half-reaction.
   Because there is one Mn on each side of the first reaction and one N on each side of the second reaction the afore reactions have already accomplished this step.

3. Add water molecules to balance the O atoms in each half-reaction.
   Because there are four O atoms on the left and two O atoms on the right of the Mn, two water molecules is added on the right side giving

$$MnO_4^{-1} \rightarrow MnO_2 + 2H_2O$$

and for the N half-reaction because there are two O on the left and three on the right we add one water to the left side giving

$$NO_2 + H_2O \rightarrow NO_3$$

4. Add H+ to each half-reaction to balance the hydrogen atoms.
   For the Mn half-reaction we add four to the left

$$4H^{+1} + MnO_4 \rightarrow MnO_2 + 2H_2O$$

and for the N half-reaction we add two to the right.

$$NO_2 + H_2O \rightarrow NO_3 + 2H^{+1}$$

5. Balance the total charge on each side by adding electrons. By charge we mean the charges of the various ions in the reaction equation-not the oxidation numbers. Thus, we want the charge on both sides of the equation to be the same.
   Thus we add 3e⁻ to the left side of the Mn half-reaction

$$3e^- + 4H^{+1} + MnO_4 \rightarrow MnO_2 + 2H_2O$$

and 2 e$^-$ to the right side of the N half-reaction.

$$NO_2 + H_2O \rightarrow NO_3 + 2H^{+1} + 2e^-$$

6. For the electrons to cancel when we add the half-reactions, we must multiply each half-reaction by a constant such that the electrons cancel out when the half-reactions are added together.

(Typically, one electron is exchanged for each oxidation number change occurring within the half cell. Thus, for the Mn half-cell, the change is from a +7 to a +4 or 3 electrons change. This agrees with what we have in step 5 above. Thus, we can ascertain the number of electrons needed in balancing the half cell in either way-either looking at number of electrons being exchanged within the individual half-cell or through balancing the charges.)

A major point in balancing redox reactions is to balance the number of electrons exchanged. Since there are three electrons in the Mn half-reaction and two electrons in the N half-reaction we will simply multiple the Mn half-reaction by 2 (because $2 \times 3e^- = 6e^-$) and the N half-reaction by 3 (because $3 \times 2e^- = 6e^-$).

$$6e^- + 8H^{+1} + 2MnO_4{}^{-1} \rightarrow 2MnO_2 + 4H_2O$$

and

$$3NO_2 + 3H_2O \rightarrow 3NO_3 + 6H^{+1} + 6e^-$$

7. Add the half-reactions together and cancel species that are the same on both sides of the equation.

$$6e^- + 8H^{+1} + 2MnO_4{}^{-1} + 3NO_2 + 3H_2O \rightarrow 2MnO_2 + 4H_2O + 3NO_3 + 6e^- + 6H^{+1}$$

This is the balanced equation.

$$2H^{+1} + 2MnO_4{}^{-1} + 3NO_2 \rightarrow 2MnO_2 + H_2O + 3NO_3$$

We can also add the K's and assuming that the acid comes from HCl giving

$$2HCl + 2KMnO_4 + 3NO_2 \rightarrow 2MnO_2 + H_2O + 3NO_3 + 2KCl$$

BATTERIES AND HARVESTING REDOX ENERGY

The exchange of electrons corresponds to energy changes that can be harvested such as in batteries. These batteries may be dry cells such as A and AA batteries, or wet cells, as in our automobile batteries.

Batteries have two electrodes-the cathode and the anode. At the **cathode-chemicals** are **reduced**, that is **electrons** are **added**. The cathode is given a **positive** sign (+). Electrons are attracted to this cathode, thus the positive sign. The **cathode takes on electrons to reduce materials**. (Remember that both the cathode and cations both have a positive sign.)

$$2NH_4{}^{+1} + 2e^- \rightarrow 2NH_3 + H_2$$

or for the lead storage battery

$$PbO_2 + 2e^- + 4H^{+1} \rightarrow Pb^{+2} + 2H_2O$$

The **anode gives up electrons** and to do this electrons must be "taken" from a material so oxidation occurs at the anode.

$$Pb \rightarrow Pb^{+2} + 2e^-$$

The **anode** is marked with a **negative** ($-$) since it gives up electrons and electrons are negatively charged. (Again, both the anode and anions have a negative sign.)

In electrolysis electrical energy (electrons) are supplied to "force" (or cause) redox to occur. Thus, the reaction of $H_2 + O_2 \rightarrow H_2O$ can be reversed by supplying electrical energy so that

$$\text{electrical energy} + 2H_2O \rightarrow 2H_2 + O_2$$

In fact, this forms the basis for the hydrolysis of water and many of the energy schemes that are being experimented with that use sunlight as the energy source. This is an electrochemical method of splitting water.

We harness the energy from exchanging electrons in all sorts of batteries. Many common dry-cell batteries, such as a AA, AAA batteries, have a graphite rod, cathode, and a zinc outer layer, anode. Electrons run from the zinc outer layer

$$Zn \rightarrow Zn^{+2} + 2e^-$$

(oxidation; anode) through whatever it is we want to power with the battery to the graphite cathode (where reaction with thick paste of ammonium chloride, zinc (II) chloride and manganese dioxide - namely the ammonium ion; cathode occurs).

$2NH_4^{+1} + 2e^- \rightarrow 2NH_3 + H_2$ but you do not smell the ammonia because it reacts with the zinc (II) chloride in the paste nor do we see bubbles of hydrogen, because of reaction with MnO_2.

$$ZnCl_2 + 2NH_3 \rightarrow Zn(NH_3)_2Cl_2 \text{ (s)}$$

$$2MnO_2 + H_2 \rightarrow Mn_2O_3 + H_2O$$

Why do we not want gases in our batteries?

Alkaline batteries operate with a greater hydroxide (thus the name alkaline meaning basic) concentration.

Oxidation; "-"; **anode** $ZnCl_2 + 2OH^{-1} \rightarrow ZnO(s) + H_2O(l) + 2e^-$

Reduction; "+"; **cathode** $2MnO_2(s) + H_2O(l) + 2e^- \rightarrow Mn_2O_3(s) + 2OH^{-1}$

Notice the cyclic nature of the system- water produced and used up, hydroxide ion used and produced.

Rechargeable batteries, like our car batteries, are able to be recharged, that is the materials used in one step to create the needed energy, are remade in another step as electrons are given back. The energy producing step is given as

$$PbO_2 + Pb + 2H_2SO_4 \rightarrow 2PbSO_4 + 2H_2O + \text{electrical energy}$$

To recharge the battery, the reverse reaction occurs, as follows.

$$\text{electrical energy} + 2PbSO_4 + 2H_2O \rightarrow PbO_2 + Pb + 2H_2SO_4$$

Many smaller rechargeable batteries are made of nickel and cadmium but the cadmium is toxic so must be monitored. An external source of electrons, such as our wall outlets, supplies the recharging.

Electrical energy can itself be used to produce chemical change. Many metals are found in nature as salts. Electrolysis is used to create the needed metal

$$Al^{+3} + 3e^- \rightarrow Al$$

Electrical energy is also part of the so-called hydrogen economy. Here hydrogen is created for later use through electrolysis of the water as we already noted.

$$\text{electrical energy} + 2H_2O \rightarrow O_2 + 2H_2$$

Combustion is a fancy name for burning.

For hydrocarbons and materials with C, H, and O in them, like wood, paper, leaves the products are carbon dioxide and water.

$$CH \text{ and } CHO + O_2 \rightarrow CO_2 + H_2O + \text{energy}$$

This is also an energy creating reaction, but not a battery and not easily reversible.

CORROSION

The control and prevention of corrosion is a major societal problem. In the midwest we see holes in automobiles and trucks with the junkyards filled with prime examples of corrosion. It has been estimated that about 20 % of the iron and steel products produced yearly in the USA replace objects that have been discarded due to rust damage. Interestingly, the rise of polymeric materials was encouraged because products made from them were lighter than similar steel and iron products and the non-susceptibility of plastics to corrosion. Even so, there are many applications where steel and iron remain the material of choice and their protection by polymeric coatings, paints, is essential for their protection. A brief listing of the amount of coatings used in the USA for various purposes is given below. This represents about 5 gallons of coatings material for everyone in the USA. Other than the home use, much of the coatings materials are employed for protection against corrosion.

Table 11.1 *USA Production of Paints and Coatings (millions of gallons).*

Architectural	668
Product	449
Special	189
Source: Department of Commerce, for 2000.	

Galvanic corrosion is the type of corrosion that destroys metallic objects including steel, iron, and other metals. For galvanic corrosion to occur, several conditions must be simultaneously present. These conditions are

- the metal is oxidized at the anode of an electrolytic cell
- ions are reduced at the cathode

- there is a sufficient potential (voltage) between the anode and the cathode to cause the flow of electrons
- an electrolyte must be present that allows for the flow of electrons, and
- the cathode and anode must be electrically connected.

For iron going to iron (II) oxide, one of the so-called compounds included under the grouping of iron rust, we have as the balanced reaction.

$$2Fe + O_2 \rightarrow 2FeO$$

For illustrations sake we can break this down into two "half-cells".
The oxidation half cell describing what is occurring at the anode is

$$Fe \rightarrow Fe^{+2} + 2e^-$$

The reduction half cell describing what is occurring at the cathode is

$$O_2 + 4e^- \rightarrow 2O^{-2}$$

The electrolyte connecting the two parts of the reaction, the electron donating portion (the oxidation half cell) and the electron devouring or consuming (the reduction half cell) can be solid, liquid, or gaseous (such as water moisture).

For metals such as iron, oxidation occurs at the surfaces. Changes brought about due to temperature and stress/strain are called "cold working" of a material.

We also resist corrosion by using certain combinations of metals. For instance, magnesium is corroded more readily than iron so that magnesium bars are often connected to iron to "save" the iron structure with the magnesium material being sacrificed. Chromium plating reduces rust formation because chromium forms a tough non-reactive, transparent oxide coating protecting the iron much like paint does. Tin is also used to form a non-reactive oxide coating on iron. However, if the surface is scratched through to the iron, the more reactive iron will rust faster than it did without the protective tin coating. Thus, tin-plated "tin-cans" readily rust once the tin-coating is compromised. In galvanizing, a thin layer of zinc coats the iron. Zinc is more reactive than iron, but it also forms a protective oxide. Here, if the oxide is penetrated, the iron will not rust until the zinc has corroded away with any iron rust that might form, reconverted into iron at the expense of the zinc. Galvanizing imparts a dull gray color to the metal and is often not considered very attractive.

Aluminum is also resistant to wholesale corrosion but through another mechanism. A cleaned strip of aluminum (lightly sanded to remove the oxide coat) will form small whitish colored crystals when exposed to bleach and household ammonia. Initially bubbles are formed and the strip will begin to turn black. Cessation of bubble formation indicates that the reaction is complete.

Again, the most widely used ploy to resist corrosion and deterioration by nature is paint. Wood is painted so that it is the paint that "experiences" the wear and tears of weathering and not the wood. For cars, the body is protected by paint, and the paint is protected by a good wax job. Today, most of the car waxes are not waxes but rather polymeric materials.

Organic Compounds

Much of what is about us is organic. We are going to pick up lots of new terms, a new language.

Unlike most elements, carbon can add to itself forming carbon chains with varying numbers of carbon atoms. The precise structure of these compounds is dependant on the particular reactants and reaction conditions. These compounds formed from a sharing of electrons between various atoms form covalently bonded compounds. These compounds form the basis of organic chemistry. The next most common element in organic compounds to carbon is hydrogen. Here we will look at some of the most important organic compounds. In other sections, namely sections 13–15 and 18, more organic compounds will be investigated.

The carbon in these organic compounds forms a total of four bonds. The carbon atoms can be bonded to four different atoms such as in methane, or three different atoms such as in ethylene, or two different atoms as in acetylene. Look for this as we investigate the wonderful world of organic compounds.

$$CH_4 \qquad H_2C = CH_2 \qquad HC \equiv CH$$
Methane   Ethylene   Acetylene

HYDROCARBONS

LINEAR HYDROCARBONS

Hydrocarbons are compounds that contain only hydrogen and carbon- CH_4 is methane, it contains only carbon and hydrogen and thus is a hydrocarbon.

Note- carbon forms 4 total bonds; oxygen two- these can be to the same or different atom.

Structural isomers means they are different compounds with different chemical and physical properties but the same formula. To transform one structural isomer into another means rearrangement of primary, covalent bonds must occur. Below are examples of structural isomers.

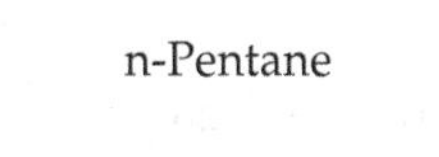

n-Pentane

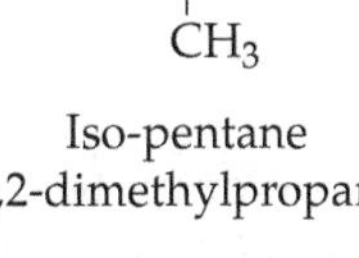

Iso-pentane
2,2-dimethylpropane

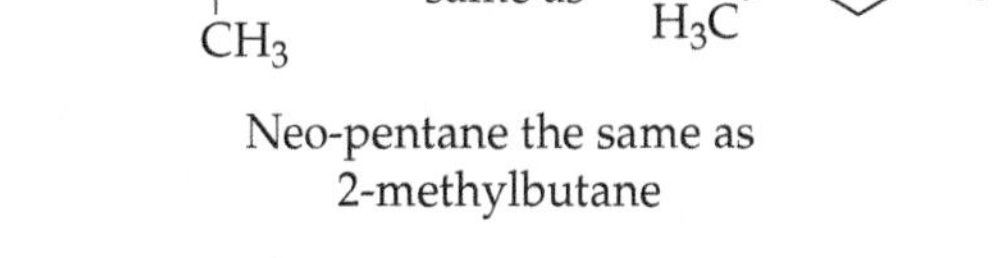

Neo-pentane the same as
2-methylbutane

The same molecule can take on different shapes-**conformations** through simple rotation about the primary bonds. Below are some structural conformations of pentane. These are the same compound.

Unsaturated means having a double or triple bond(s) present. Remember, double bonds have both a sigma bond and a pi bond. These double bonds are not freely movable because the parallel overlapping p-orbitals forming the pi bond are not able to freely rotate. Thus, there are what are called cis and trans structural isomers. These are different compounds with different chemical and physical properties.

Trans (across)   Cis

Table 12.1 *Typical Straight Chain Hydrocarbon Fractions Obtained from Distillation of Petroleum Resources.*

Boiling range, °C	Average number of carbon atoms	Name	Uses
<30	1–4	Gas	Heating
30–180	5–10	Gasoline	Automotive fuel
180–230	11, 12	Kerosene	Jet fuel, heating
230–300	13–17	Light gas oil	Diesel fuel, heating
300–400	18–25	Heavy gas oil	Heating

CYCLIC HYDROCARBONS

Benzene is an example of a cyclic compound as is cyclohexane.

When there are two or more substituents on the ring the positions of the substituents are variously named according to their locations. Some important substituted benzene derivatives are given below.

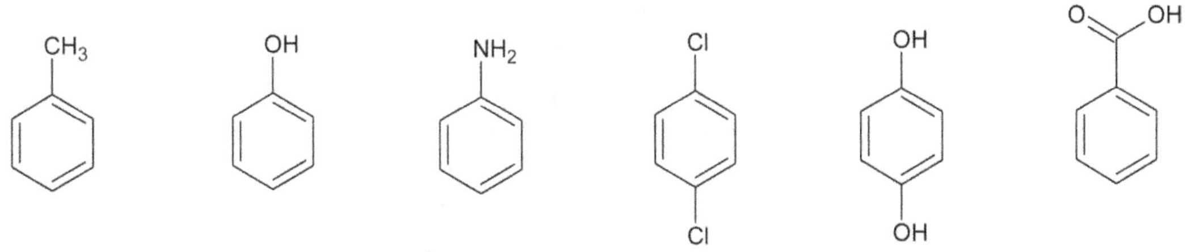

| Toluene | Phenol | Aminobenzene | 1,3-Dichlorobenzene | Hydroquinone | Benzoic Acid |

They were originally called aromatic because many of them gave off odors, they smelled.

FUNCTIONAL GROUPS

We need to know about functional groups. We will use an R to represent some undefined other moiety. Thus for ethanol, CH_3CH_2OH we can let it be represented as ROH. Diethylether, $C_2H_5OC_2H_5$, can be represented by ROR.

Following, Table 12.2, are important functional groups we will deal with and which you should know how to identify when given compounds containing them.

Table 12.2 *Listing of important functional groups.*

Alcohol R—OH or ROH

Ether ROR or R—O—R

Amine RNH_2

Ketone R—C—R′   The "C" is often called a carbonyl group.
(with O double-bonded to C)

Aldehyde R—C—H
(with O double-bonded to C)

Amide R—N—C—R′
(with H on N and O double-bonded to C)

Carboxyl (carboxylic acids) R—C—O—H
(with O double-bonded to C)

Ester R—C—O—R′
(with O double-bonded to C)

Organic halides R—X where X = F, Cl, Br, I, such as R—Cl

Many compounds contain more than one functional group such as morphine that has an amine, two alcohols and an ether along with an aromatic ring and another site of unsaturation.

ALCOHOLS

Most organic compounds have both a common name that we are often familiar with and a formal name that is in accord with the official scientific naming organization the International Union of Pure and Applied Chemistry, IUPAC. The functional group within alcohols is actually called a hydroxyl, -OH, group. Notice that the formal names of alcohols have an "ol" ending. Here we will describe the most common alcohols. **Methyl alcohol**, methanol, is used as a solvent for shellac and other coatings (paints) when the coating is intended to be fast drying. This is because methyl alcohol evaporates rapidly because of its low boiling point. It is also used as an additive to antifreeze and as a fuel. Methyl alcohol, methanol, is also known as **wood alcohol** because it can be obtained from the burning of wood.

Ethyl alcohol, ethanol, can be made from the fermentation of sugars and other carbohydrates. It is the alcohol in beer, wine, rum, and whiskey. Non-drinking alcohol is widely used as a solvent and starting material for many more complex compounds. Commercially it is made from ethane. The topic of ethyl alcohol is further covered in the section on drugs.

Isopropyl alcohol, 2-propanol, is used as a solvent for oils and paints. Mixtures containing about 60–70% isopropyl alcohol in water are sold as **rubbing alcohol** and used as a disinfectant. **Ethylene glycol**, 1,2-ethanediol, is mainly used as the major ingredient in permanent automotive antifreezes and summer coolants. Its high boiling point, low freezing point, readily availability at a low cost lends to its widespread use as a solvent and as one of the two major ingredients in the manufacture of the most widely used **polyester poly(ethylene terephthalate)**, PET or PETE, which is used to make polyester rugs and most of the soda and water drinking bottles. It has a sweet taste and looks like water, so each year a number of children and pets accidentally drink it causing them to become blind or to die.

Glycerol, also called glycerin, 1,2,3-propanetriol, is used to sweeten toothpaste and in many cosmetics. It is a byproduct of soap manufacture. It is also used to make trinitroglycerin also known as nitroglycerin, a highly shock and heat sensitive explosive. Alfred Nobel built much of his industrial empire on nitroglycerin. It is often obtained from fats since it forms an essential structural unit in fats. The concentration of ethyl alcohol is often described in terms of proof. **Proof** is simply the percentage alcohol times two. Thus, a 3% beer is 6 proof.

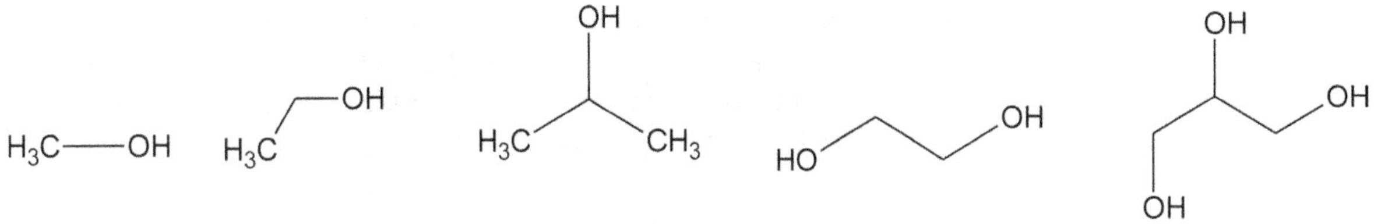

Ethyl Alcohol   Ethyl Alcohol Isopropyl Alcohol Ethylene Glycol   Glycerol

Each of the alcohols is somewhat toxic. Table 1 contains a general human toxic dosage for some of these alcohols. The low toxicity of glycerol is expected since it forms one of the major structural components in fats and is naturally make by our body.

Table 12.3 *Estimated lethal dose for selected alcohols.*

Alcohol	Estimated Lethal Dose, oral
Methanol	3–30 g
Isopropanol	30–300 g
Ethylene glycol	300–500 g
Ethanol	1,000–9,000 g
Glycerol	>9,000 g

THIOLS

Thiols, R-SH, are structurally similar to alcohol except the oxygen is now a sulfur or thiol. These compounds are also called mercaptans. Most have a strong repulsive odor like a skunk or rotten egg. They are added to odorless gasses such as natural gas to alert a person to the presence of the odorless natural gas. Many are quite toxic but because of their smelly nature, people leave the area before they are killed.

CARBONYL COMPOUNDS

Carbonyl- The carbonyl grouping, C=O, is the main functional group for aldehydes and ketones. It is also present in organic acids, esters, and amides, but each of these will be dealt with in a separate section. For the **aldehydes,** one of the connective groups must be a hydrogen atom. If both connective groups to the carbonyl are hydrogen atoms then the compound is formaldehyde or methanal. Formaldehyde is a gas but is often dissolved in about a 40% water solution giving a mixture called formalin. Formaldehyde is used to kill germs and as a preservative for biological tissues. Formaldehyde self polymerizes to form polyoxymethylene which is sold as Delrin and is known in labs as parafilm.

Formaldehyde Acetaldehyde   Polyoxymethylene

Formaldehyde is also used to form a number of important thermoset polymers including phenolic resins that are used to bind together thin sheets of wood to form plywood. These phenolic resins are given the name Bakelite. Reaction of formaldehyde with melamine and urea gives products called urea and melamine thermosets that are used to bind together paper to form laminated countertops and plastics used to make dinnerware such as plates. The urea-formaldehyde materials are used to make particle board as are other formaldehyde products.

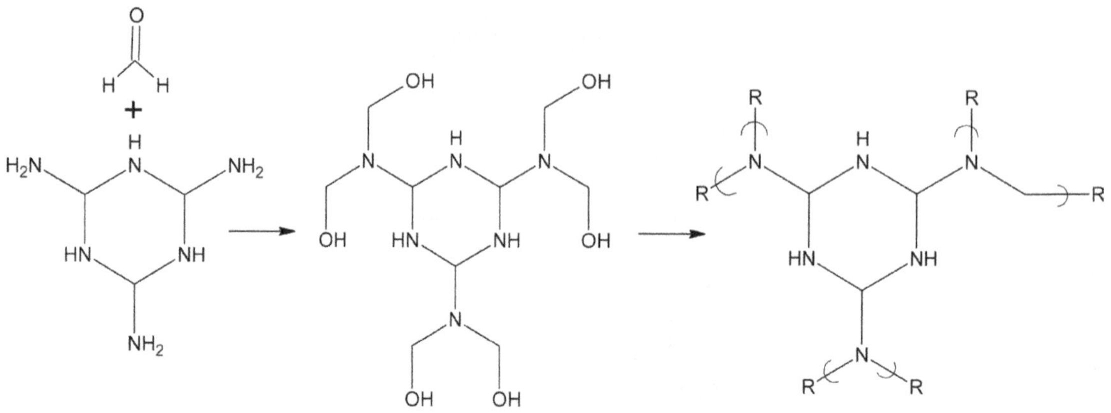

Figure 12.1 *Crosslinked melamine-formaldehyde*

Acetaldehyde is a major degradation product of ethyl alcohol. As ethyl alcohol is oxidized it forms a variety of materials including acetaldehyde. These breakdown products are responsible for the bitter taste that some ethyl alcohol (such as wines) has.

Aldehydes are also prevalent as food flavoring agents. Benzaldehyde is used as an almond flavor, cinnamaldehyde as a cinnamon flavor, and vanillin as a vanilla flavor.

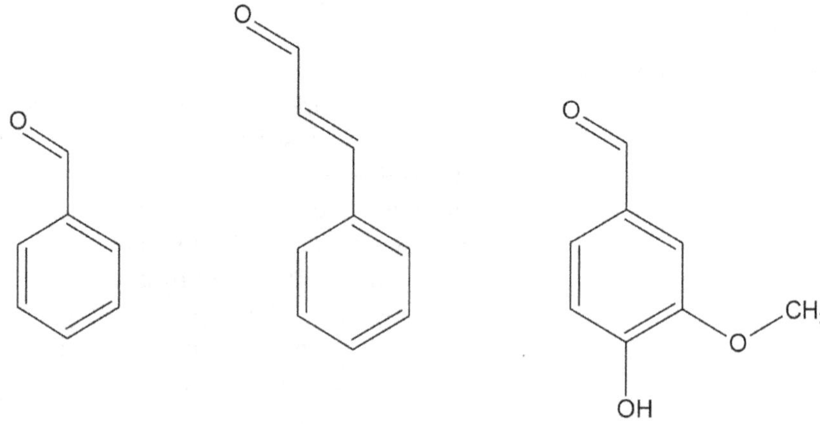

Benzaldehyde   Cinnamaldehyde   Vanillin

The other carbonyl grouping is the **ketones** where neither group connected to the carbonyl is a hydrogen. The most common ketone is acetone, propanone. Notice that the formal name for ketones have an "one" ending. Acetone is a major industrial solvent and is used in paint removers, nail polish removers, and in nail polish formulations.

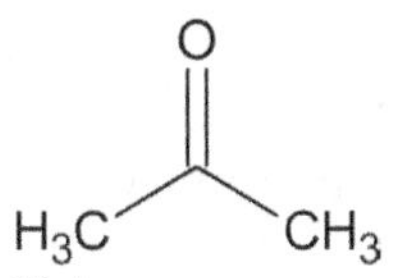

Ketone

Carboxyl group- The carboxyl group, –COOH, forms the basis of **organic acids** and their salts. **Formic acid**, methanoic acid, is the simplest of the acids. It is present in the sting of some wasps, bees, and ants. It stimulates the pain-sensing nerve endings by lowering the pH. Body water flows into the stung area to dilute the formic acid helping cause blister formation. The best treatment is to add a little baking soda, $NaHCO_3$, which neutralizes the formic acid. The Latin word *formica* means ant and formic acid was so named because it was initially isolated from the distillation of ants. Insect bites also inject other materials including proteins that can interact with our immune system casing severe allergic reactions in some people. Formic acid is used in the commercial production of dyes, perfumes, drugs, and polymers.

Acetic acid, ethanoic acid, is the most widely used organic acid. Along with water, it is the major ingredient in vinegar. Vinegar can contain little or a lot of acetic acid. It is formed from the degradation of many fruits. Apples are the main source of commercial vinegar. Acetic acid is a weak acid, weaker than formic acid. Acid strength is measured in terms of the ionization, that is the formation of ions, here protons, when the chemical is added to water. This ionization process is reversible and in fact exists as a dynamic equilibrium. Two arrows going in opposite directions is used to signal that the process is an equilibrium process. Since acetic acid is a weak acid, most of acetic acid exists in the non-charged form on the left with only a low amount existing in the charged or deprotonated state shown on the right side.

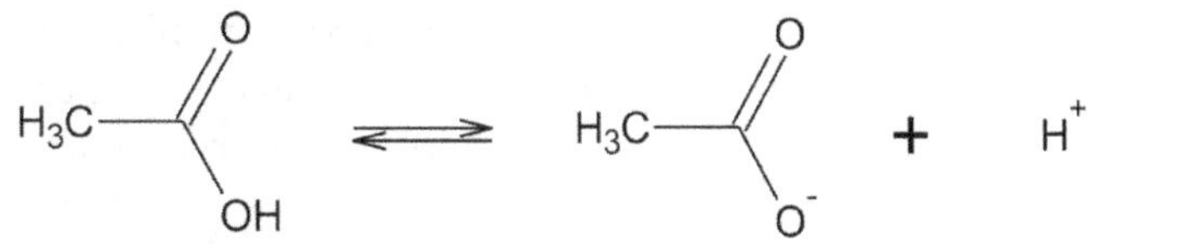

Non-ionized Acetic Acid   Ionized Form   Proton

Benzoic acid is the best known aromatic acid. These acids are called aromatic acids because most of them emit an odor. When reacted with sodium hydroxide, benzoic acid forms a salt, sodium benzoate which is used as a common food additive to fight bacteria. It is also used to inhibit rust and mildew and in perfumes, drugs, polymers, and flavors.

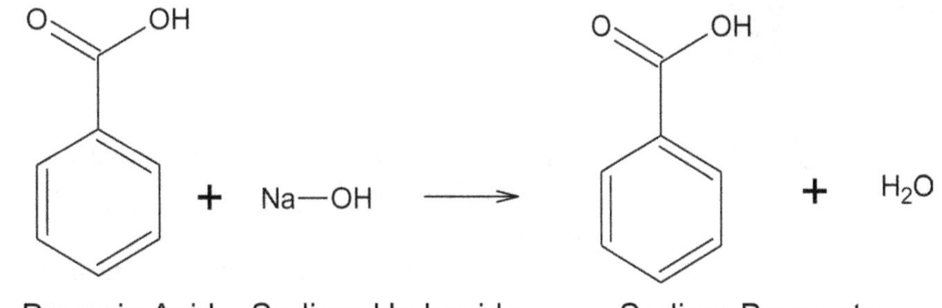

Benzoic Acid   Sodium Hydroxide   Sodium Benzoate

AMINES

Amines- Unlike most of the other functional groups, amines are subdivided into primary, RNH_2; secondary, R_2NH; and tertiary R_3N, amines depending on the number of non-hydrogen atoms connected to the nitrogen. Amines also form salts that are known as quaternary amines. Amines are found in many drugs. Amines are organic bases meaning they will accept a proton, generally from an acid or other proton-donating compound. An important illustration of this is pictured below where the neutral amino acid glycine generally exists as a zwitterion as pictured to the right. This behavior is common for amino acids and enhances their already good water solubility because of the formation of the two charged ends that strongly interact with the polar water molecules.

Another major use of amines is as reactants to form polyamides. Natural polyamides are also given the names of polypeptides and proteins. Synthetic polyamines are often given the name nylons. More about these important materials in the sections on polymers and amines for the nylons and in section 13 for the proteins.

One of the earliest chemical industries was the dye or color industry. Initially, colorants were natural, generally extracted from natural materials that were colored. Thus, alizarin, a red dye, is extracted from the madder plant roots and indigo, a blue dye, from the *Indigofera* plant. In the 1850's Perkin was experimenting with trying to synthesize quinine, a drug used in the treatment of malaria. Instead, he synthesized a material that was a rich purple when added to ethyl alcohol. He named this new material mauve. In later years, Perkin synthesized a number of other dyes helping found the dye industry. Mauve has a primary, 1, secondary, 2, and tertiary, 3, amine as well as an amine salt, 4, known as a quaternary amine.

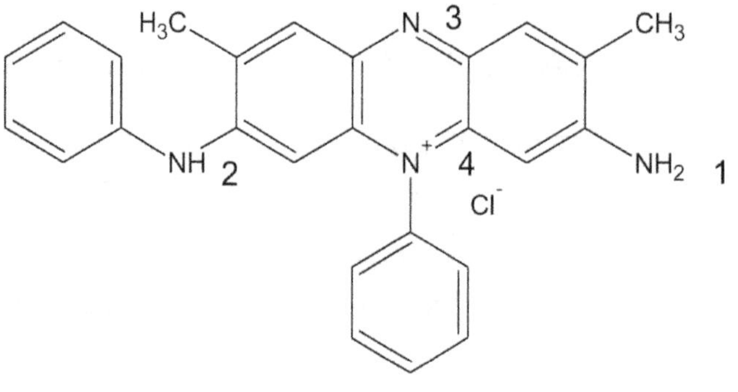

Mauve

ESTERS

There are several "compound" functional groups created from the reaction of two other functional groups. Two of these will be presented– the esters and amides.

Functional groups can react with one another forming different functional groups. The reaction between an alcohol and acid gives an ester. Ethyl acetate and methyl acetate are important industrial solvents. Ethyl acetate is also used in model paint and in model airplane glue.

Acetic Acid   Ethyl Alcohol   Ethyl Acetate

Volatile esters often have attractive odors and are employed in perfumes.

Banana   Pear   Lemon

Peppermint   Wintergreen   Jasmine

In nature, fatty esters are formed from the reaction of fats and glycerol.

Just as the reaction between alcohols and acids each containing a single functional group occurs to give small distinct molecules, the reaction between alcohols and acids each containing two functional groups, that is diols and diacids, can produce polymers because reaction occurs at each end eventually giving long polyester chains. Initially, the individual diacids and diols react giving an ester with alcohol and an acid ends.

$$\underset{\text{HO–C–R–C–OH}}{\overset{\text{O}\quad\text{O}}{\overset{\|\quad\|}{}}} + \text{HO–R}'\text{–OH} \rightleftharpoons \underset{\text{HO–C–R–C–O–R}'\text{–OH}}{\overset{\text{O}\quad\text{O}}{\overset{\|\quad\|}{}}} + \text{H}_2\text{O}$$

This ester-containing unit can now react with either an alcohol or acid group producing chains ending with either two active alcohol functional groups or two active acid groups

HOC(O)-R-C(O)-R'-OH + HO-R'-OH $\rightleftharpoons$ HO-R'-O-C(O)-R-C(O)-O-R'-OH + H_2O
or

HO-C(O)-R-C(O)-R'-OH + HO-C(O)-R-C(O)-OH $\rightleftharpoons$
HO-C(O)-R-C(O)-O-R'-O-C(O)-R-C(O)-OH +H_2O

These units can then again react.

HO–R'–O–C(O)–R–C(O)–O–R'–OH + HO–C(O)–R–C(O)–OH $\rightleftharpoons$

HO–R'–O–C(O)–R–C(O)–O–R'–O–C(O)–R–C(O)–OH + H_2O
and

HO-C(O)-R-C(O)-O-R'-O-C(O)-R-C(O)-OH + HO-R'-OH $\rightleftharpoons$

HO-C(O)-R-C(O)-O-R'-O-C(O)-R-C(O)-O-R'-OH + H_2O

Eventually a polyester is formed with a repeat unit –(-O-R'-O-C(O)-R-C-(O)-)- occurring hundreds and thousands of times within the same chain.

The most widely used polyester is formed from the reaction of ethylene glycol, a diol, and terephthalic acid, a diacid, forming poly(ethylene terephthalate), PET or PETE. As a fiber it was first sold under the trade name Dacron and as a plastic it was initially sold under the trade name Mylar. PET is a major polymer used to make fibers for clothing and carpets and plastics such as soda bottles.

Terephthalic Acid   Ethylene glycol   Poly(ethylene terephthalate)
PET, PETE

AMIDES

Another combined functional group is the amide. It is formed from the reaction of an amine and an acid group. Mono-functional amines and acids form small molecules whereas diamines and diacids can form polymers. In polymers they form the basis for the synthetic nylons and in nature they appear as polypeptides and proteins.

The most widely used synthetic nylon in the US is nylon 6,6 formed from reaction between 1,6-hexamethylene diamine and adipic acid.

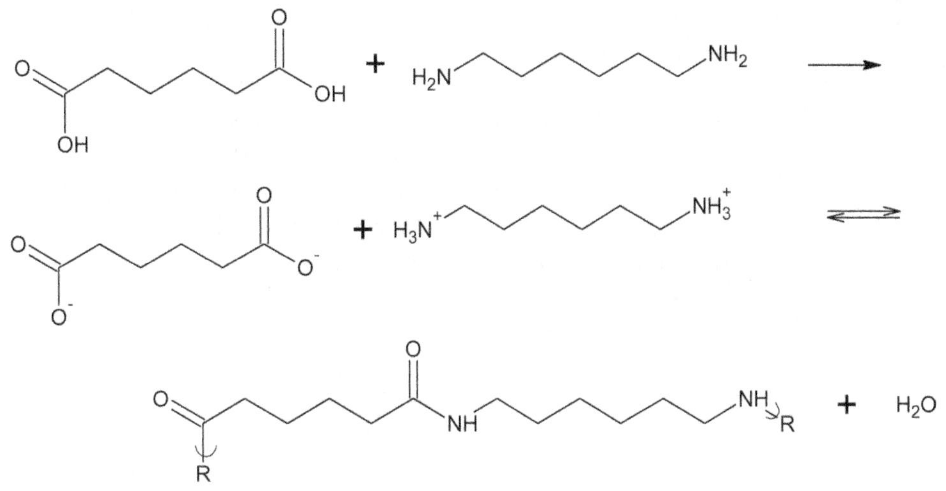

Nylon 6,6

The first number in the nylon name corresponds to the number of carbons in the diamine- six. The second number corresponds to the number of carbons in the acid, here also 6.

In order to get around patient rights held by Dupont, companies in Europe use nylon 6 instead of nylon 6,6. Nylon 6 is structurally similar to and has properties similar to nylon 6,6 but is made from cyclic compounds.

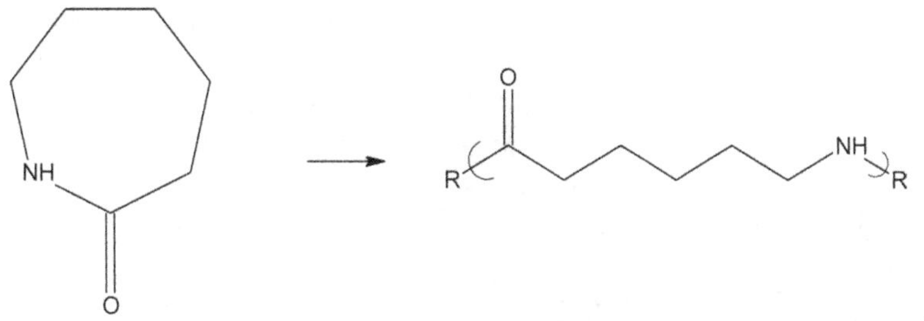

Nylon-6

Nylon 6 and nylon 6,6 are known as aliphatic nylons. Aromatic nylons have aromatic units in place of the aliphatic units and are known as **aramids**. Poly(m-phenylene isophthalamide) is sold under the tradename of Nomex. It is used in flame-resistant clothing. It is also used in the form of thin pads to protect sintered silica–fiber mats from stress and vibrations during the flight of the space shuttle.

Isophthaloyl Chloride + m-Phenylenediamine→Poly(m-phenylene isophthalamide)

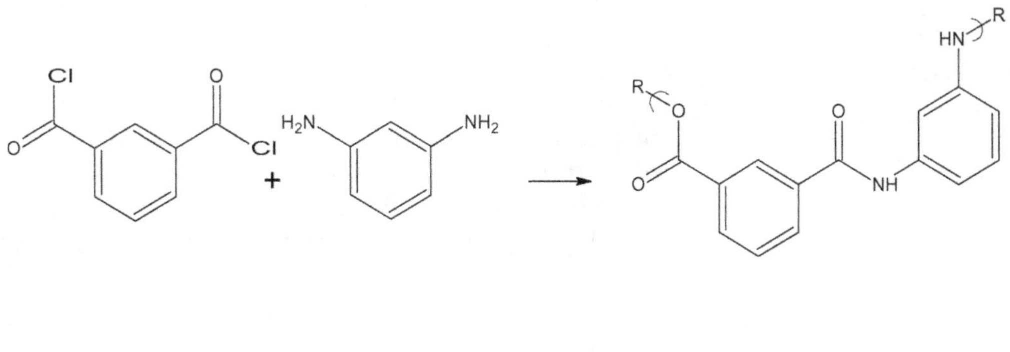

The corresponding aramid produced using the para reactant in place of the meta gives poly(p-phenylene terephthalamide), PPT, produced under the trademark of Kevlor. By weight it has a higher strength and modulus than steel and is used in the manufacture of so-called "bullet-proof" clothing. Because of its outstanding strength, it was used as the skin covering of the Gossamer Albatross which was flown, using only human-power, across the English Channel. Aramids are also used as fiber reinforcement in composites and as tire cord.

Terephthaloyl Chloride   +   p-Phenylenediamine   —>   Poly(p-phenylene terephthalamide) (PPT)

POLYMERS-INTRODUCTION

We have already been introduced to some important polymers in the preceding sections including nylons and polyesters. Here we will have a more in depth look at polymers because of their importance in our lives.

Many of the most important materials about us are polymeric-natural like polysaccharides (cellulose and starch), nucleic acids (DNA, RNA), and proteins (composed of amide units like nylon), inorganic (like glass, quartz, granite, cement, diamond, graphite, carbon nanotubes), and synthetic organic polymers.

Today, nearly 10,000 American companies are active in the general area of synthetic polymers. Following is a brief description of these companies divided according to their function.

Manufacturers: There are over 200 major manufacturers of general purpose polymers and numerous other manufacturers of specialty polymers.

Processors: Some companies manufacture their own polymeric materials for subsequent processing, but the majority purchases the necessary polymeric materials from other companies. Processors may specialize in the use of selected polymers, such as nylons and polycarbonates, or focus on particular techniques of processing, such as coatings, films, sheets, laminates, and bulk molded and reinforced plastics.

Fabricators and finishers: The majority of companies are involved in the fabrication and finishing of polymers, i.e., production of the end products for industrial and general public consumption. Fabrication can be divided into three broad areas: machining, forming, and fashioning. Machining includes grinding, sawing, screwing, and other techniques. Forming includes molding and other methods of shaping and joining by welding, gluing, screwing, and other techniques. Fashioning includes cutting, sewing, sheeting, and sealing. Fabrication sequences vary with the polymeric material and desired end product.

While much classic polymer technology was developed without the benefit of science, modern polymer technology and polymer science are closely associated. Chemistry is moving center-stage in many areas of medicine, biology, engineering, environmental science, and physics.

Polymers can be divided in many ways. One of these is related to their ability to be reformed (recycled) on application of heat and pressure. Those polymers that can be reformed on application of heat and pressure are called **thermoplastics**. These materials are generally linear and can be somewhat easily recycled and include most of the materials with a prefix "poly" such as polyethylene, polystyrene, and polypropylene as well as the polyesters and nylons. These linear polymers can be considered as strings or chains. These chains undergo a transition where at lower temperatures there is no mobility but as the temperature is raised, there is sufficient energy to allow local or segmental mobility of the chain parts but not mobility of the entire chain or string. This transition is referred to as the **glass transition temperature**, T_g. Linear polymers typically have a T_g so can be reformed as the material is heated. The other category includes materials that do not soften when heated and these polymers are called **thermoset** polymers because their shape is set when the monomers or pre-polymers are placed in a mold and heat applied. These materials are generally crosslinked forming chains that are chemically bonded to one another at many junctures. They do not melt when heated forming only char from their decomposition and so are more difficult to recycle. Bakelite and most rubbers are thermoset polymers.

Polymers abound as synthetic materials. They are also plentiful as natural materials as inorganic polymers and as organic natural materials such as cellulose, starch, proteins, and nucleic acids. Inorganic polymers are the major components of soil, mountains, and sand. Inorganic polymers are also extensively employed as abrasives and cutting materials [diamond, boron carbide, silicon carbide (Carborundum), aluminum oxide], coatings, flame retardants, building and construction materials (window glass, stone, Portland cement, brick, tiles), and lubricants and catalysts (zinc oxide, nickel oxide, carbon black, graphite, silica gel, alumina, aluminum silicate, chromium oxides, clays). Here we will look at some synthetic and inorganic polymers.

ORGANIC POLYMERS

VINYL POLYMERS

Vinyl polymers is the name given to polymers that are derived from reactants, monomers, that usually contain a C=C grouping called the vinyl group. Thus, polyethylene is formed from reaction of ethylene monomers.

$H_2C=CH_2$ → -(-CH_2-CH_2-)-

Poly(vinyl chloride) is formed from the monomer vinyl chloride.

$H_2C=CHCl$ →   -(-CH_2-CH-)-
                            |
                            Cl

Most of the common items about us are polymeric, and many are derived from vinyl monomers (Table 12.2).

Table 12.2 *Commercially important vinyl polymers.*

Name	Repeat Unit
Polyethylene, PE	$-CH_2-CH_2-$
Polypropylene, PP	$-CH_2-CH-$ $\mid$ CH_3
Polystyrene, PS	$-CH_2-CH-$ $\mid$ Ph
Poly(vinyl chloride), PVC	$-CH_2-CH-$ $\mid$ Cl
Polytetrafluoroethylene, Teflon	$-CF_2-CF_2-$
Poly(methyl methacrylate), PMMA	$-CH_2-CH-$ $\mid$ $O=C-O-CH_3$
Poly(vinyl acetate)	$-CH_2-CH-$ $\mid$ $O-C=O$ $\mid$ CH_3

The polymers synthesized in the largest amounts are the polyethylenes, PE. The two largest used PEs are high density PE, HDPE which is largely linear, strong, less soluble, higher melting, than the low density PE, LDPE, which has more branching making it less well ordered, less crystalline, more amorphous, lower melting, more flexible, not as strong, and more soluble.

The starting materials are called monomers and hence the name polymer where "poly" means many and "mer" means units. The length is called the degree of polymerization, DP. The monomer units add forming the polymer in what is called a heat-to-tail fashion so that the repeat unit for the polymerization of the monomer propylene is polypropylene and is

$$-CH_2-CH(CH_3)-CH_2-CH(CH_3)-CH_2-CH(CH_3)-CH_2-CH(CH_3)- \text{ NOT}$$
$$-CH(CH_3)-CH_2-CH_2-CH(CH_3)-CH(CH_3)-CH_2-CH_2-CH(CH_3)-$$

CONDENSATION POLYMERS

Condensation polymers also include some common materials that form fibers and plastics. Most of the natural polymers are condensation polymers. The fibers in rugs can be synthetic polymers such as polyesters or polyamides (nylons) or can be natural condensation polymers such as wool, silk, and cotton. We have already encountered polyamides (nylons) and polyesters.

The condensation polymers generally have non-carbon atoms in their backbone and are called condensation polymers because most of them give off a condensate or small units like water when formed.

Thus, nylons can be made as follows:

SECTION 12 ■ *Organic Compounds*   **97**

$$HOOC-R-COOH + H_2N-R'-NH_2 \longrightarrow -(\overset{\overset{O}{\|}}{C}-R-\overset{\overset{O}{\|}}{C}-NH-R'-NH-)- + H_2O$$

The amide linkage C(O)-NH is the same linkage that appears in proteins except here it is referred to as a peptide linkage.

Your CDs are largely composed of polycarbonates.

Polycarbonate

Crosslinked polymers are formed if the functionality, number of reactive groups, on one monomer is two and the other is three or greater. Remember, thermoset polymers are more difficult to recycle because they do not deform or melt when heat and pressure are applied.

CARBON INTENSE INORGANIC POLYMERS

There are a number of carbon polymers that contain mostly or only carbon atoms joined in various ways. These include graphite and diamonds. In diamonds each carbon is present as a tetrahedral and connected to four other carbon atoms. Graphite contains carbon atoms bonded to three other carbon atoms forming sheets that are connected by a weak overlapping of pi electrons. It can be looked at as sheets of hexagonally fused benzene rings or "hexachicken wire." Because the sheets are connected by weak bonds graphite acts as a slippery materials because the sheets easily slip past one another. By comparison, diamond is the hardest material known because of the rigidity and three dimensional nature of the tetrahedral carbon atoms.

Natural diamonds are believed to have been formed millions of years ago when concentrations of pure carbon were subjected by the Earth's mantle to great pressures and heat. The majority of diamonds (non-gem) are now man-made. Most of the synthetic diamonds are no larger than a grain of common sand. The major use of synthetic diamonds is as industrial shaping and cutting agents to cut, grind, and bore (drill). By 1970 General Electric was manufacturing diamonds of gem quality and size through compressing pure carbon under extreme pressure and heat. It was found that addition of small amounts of boron to diamonds causes them to become semiconductors. Today, such doped diamonds are used to make transistors.

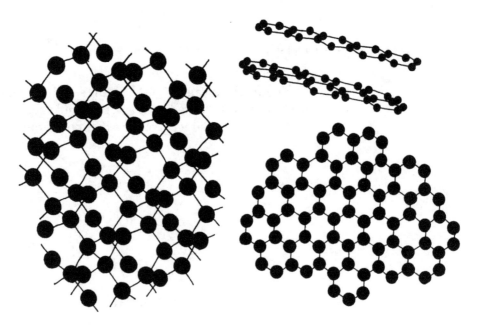

Figure 12.2 *Diamond Molecular Structure, left; and Graphite Molecular Structure (layered (top) and sheet (bottom) right)*

Carbon also forms the basis of the bitumens. Bitumens have been used for thousands of years and are still used today. They were used in the waterproofing of the cradle that baby Moses was floated in. Bitumen was used by the ancient Egyptians in their mummification process. Bitumens were used in sand stabilization and for lighting the naval base by the Second Muslim Caliph, Omar ben Khattab, at Basra on Shattul-Arab on the West Coast of what is now Saudi Arabia around 640 AD.

Bitumens occur naturally or are formed as the residue in the distillation of coal tar, petroleum, etc. Industrially, the two most important bitumens are asphalt and coal tar. Asphalt is a brown to black tar-like variety of bitumen that again occurs naturally or is the residue of distillation. Coal tar is the black, thick-liquid obtained as the residue from the distillation of bituminous coal. Many of our roads are "tarred" with bitumen.

Today, another wholly carbon polymer is becoming one of the most important materials of the 21st century, carbon nanotubes. Carbon nanotubes, CNTs, can be single walled or multiple walled. They can be thought of as being formed from closed carbon rings called fullerenes. Depending on the fullerene three general forms of CNTs can be made. These forms are the armchair, zizzag, and helical. Each form has its own set of properties. Carbon nanotubes are relatively quite strong, flexible, and some can conduct electricity. Thus, they can be made to be molecular conductive wires that can be turned off by bending them. They can hold drugs within their hollow tubes delivering drugs on a molecular level. They can also hold hydrogen so may be part of fuel cells. They are used today as tips in atomic force microscopes. Pants and shirts have been made from carbon nanotubes.

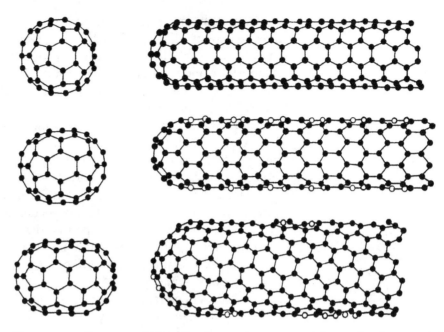

Figure 12.3 *Representations of the three major structural forms of carbon nanotubes: armchair (top), zigzag (middle), and helical (bottom) and of C_{60} (left, top), C_{70} (left, middle), and C_{80} (left, bottom) fullerene structures.*

SILICON-CONTAINING POLYMERS

There are a number of important silicon-intense polymers. These polymers are generally based on silicon and oxygen. Here we will look at some of these.

Portland cement is the least expensive, most widely used synthetic inorganic polymer. It is employed as the basic nonmetallic, non-woody material of construction. Concrete highways and streets span our country side and concrete skyscrapers silhouette the urban skyline. Less spectacular uses are found in everyday life as sidewalks, fence posts, and parking bumpers.

The name "Portland" is derived from the cement having the same color as the natural stone quarried on the Isle of Portland, a peninsula on the south of Great Britain. The word cement comes from the Latin word *caementum*, which means "pieces of rough, uncut stone." Concrete comes from the Latin word *concretus*, meaning "to grow together."

Common (dry) cement consists of anhydrous crystalline calcium silicates (the major ones being tricalcium silicate, Ca_3SiO_5, and β-dicalcium silicate, Ca_2SiO_4), lime (CaO, 60%), and alumina (a complex aluminum silicate, 5%). When anhydrous cement mix is added to water, the silicates react, forming hydrates and calcium hydroxide. Hardened Portland cement contains about 70% crosslinked calcium silicate hydrate and 20% crystalline calcium hydroxide.

Most of our rocks are based on silicon-oxygen compounds called silicates. These materials can be three-dimensional, two-dimensional sheets, and one-dimensional chains. Quart is an important network silicate. These networks have molecular holes in them that accommodate other elements. Feldspars have sodium and aluminum as well as silicon and oxygen. Many of the clay materials consist of layered silicates with different metal ions connecting the layers.

One of the most important inorganic polymers is amorphous silicon dioxide known as glass. Much of the sand at our beaches is amorphous silicon dioxide. Glass has many useful properties. It ages (changes chemical composition and physical property) slowly, typically retaining its fine optical and hardness-related properties for centuries. Glass is referred to as a supercooled liquid or a very viscous liquid. Indeed, it is a slow-moving liquid. Consistent with this is the observation that the old stained glass windows adorning European cathedrals are a little thicker at the bottom of each small, individual piece than at the top of the piece. For most purposes though, glass can be treated as a brittle solid that shatters on sharp impact.

Glass is mainly silica sand (SiO_2) and is made by heating silica sand and powdered additives together in a specified manner and proportion much as a cake is baked, following a recipe that describes the items to be included, amounts, mixing procedure (including sequence), oven temperature, and heating time. The amounts, nature of additives, etc., all affect the physical properties of the final glass.

Typically cullet, recycled or waste glass (5-40%), is added along with the principle raw materials (mostly SiO_2). The mixture is thoroughly mixed and then added to a furnace where the mixture is heated to near 1500°C to form a viscous, syrup-like liquid. The size and nature of the furnace corresponds to the glasses' intended uses. For small, individual items the mixture may be heated in a small clay (refractory) pot.

Most glass is melted in large (continuous) tanks that can melt 400–600 metric tons a day for production of other glass products. The process is continuous with the raw materials fed into one end as molten glass is removed from the other end. Once the process (called a campaign) is begun it is continued indefinitely, night and day, often for several years until the demand is met or the furnace breaks down.

Today, safety glass is divided into three general categories, laminated safety glass, tempered safety glass, and armed glass. **Laminated safety glass** is composed of sheets of glass held together by poly(vinyl butyral).

Poly(vinyl alcohol)/butyraldehyde   Poly(vinyl butyral)

Tempered safety glass is made by heating the glass to its melting point, about 700°C, and then cooling it rapidly by blowing cold air onto its surfaces. The effect is similar to the production of stressed concrete where the concrete is allowed to harden under stress giving a stronger concrete. In the case of glass, when it is rapidly cooled, a structure is locked in that produces extra stress on the glass structure making it stronger. As the glass is cooled, the surfaces harden first locking in the overall glass volume. As the center cools, it forces the surfaces and edges into compression. With appropriate rapid cooling, the glass is not only stronger, but when shattered, produces granulates rather than sharp cutting shards. The typical force necessary to break tempered glass is about four times that required to shatter ordinary glass of the same thickness.

While the front "windshield" is made of safety glass, the remainder of the automotive glass windows are generally made from tempered glass. Tempered glass is also used for commercial building doors and windows, sidelights, patio-door assemblies, storm doors, shower and tub enclosures, refrigerator, oven, and stove shelves, and fireplace screens.

Crystalline silicon dioxide is known as quartz. There are several forms of quartz.

Polysiloxanes, also called **silicones**, are characterized by combinations of chemical, mechanical, and electrical properties which taken together are not common to any other commercially available class of polymers. They exhibit relatively high thermal and oxidative stability, low power loss, high dielectric strength, and unique flow properties, and are relatively inert to most ionic reagents. Almost all of the commercially utilized siloxanes are based on polydimethylsiloxane with trimethylsiloxy end groups. They have the widest use temperature range for commercial polymers suitable for outdoor applications from the winter of Nome Alaska to the summer of south Florida. The first footprints on the moon were made with polysiloxane elastomeric boots.

Natural Materials

There are a number of main groups of natural materials. Some of these will be covered in this section namely saccharides (more familiar to us as carbohydrates; including polysaccharides such as cellulose and starch), lipids, steroids, nucleic acids (DNA, RNA) and proteins (natural polyamides). Most of these are polymeric or macromolecules (macro = large). Just as synthetic polymers are made from basic building units, mers or monomers, the polymeric natural materials are made from smaller building blocks.

CARBOHYDRATES (SACCHARIDES)

The monomers of many of the polysaccharides or polycarbohydrates are called simple sugars and include our table sugar sucrose, a disaccharide meaning made up of two ringed systems, which is made from two monosaccharides, glucose and fructose.

Glucose   Fructose

Sucrose

The glucose unit forms the foundation for three of the most important complex carbohydrates. These are starch, cellulose, and glycogen. Polymeric polysaccharides are called **complex polysaccharides** while the mono and disaccharides are referred to as **simple saccharides**. All three of these can be degraded to give glucose the major energy molecule in nature. **Starch** is the plant storage chemical for glucose. While essentially all plants have starch, we receive much of our starch from potatoes. Potatoes have two main forms of starch. The first form composes about 20% of the starch and is called amylose. **Amylose** exists in a largely coiled or helical geometry. Because of the regularity of the helical structure, amylase is considered to be crystalline. The other form, composing about 80% of the starch, is amylopectin. **Amylopectin** is generally helical but with branches forming an amorphous, irregular structure. The ends of starch are the sites where degradation eventually to glucose begins. Because of the increased branching in amylopectin, it is able to more rapidly supply glucose in comparison to amylase. You can get an idea that glucose is being formed by placing some bread in your mouth for a few minutes while the enzymes cause a breakdown to glucose indicated by a somewhat sweet taste.

Glycogen is often referred to as animal starch. It has a structure similar to amylopectin but with more branching. Glycogen serves as our glucose reserve. Our muscle tissue and liver are the sites in our body where glycogen is most abundant.

The third complex carbohydrate is **cellulose** that is the most abundant renewable resource. It is a major constituent in plants. The somewhat linear cellulose chains internally form hydrogen bonds with other cellulose chains making it water insoluble. Cellulose is used in the textile industry in cloths, cartons, carpets, blankets, and sheets. Paper is made from cellulose. Cellulosic fibers are also used as filter materials in artificial kidneys and reverse osmosis though today most kidney dialysis units use films derived from cellulose rather than cellulose itself.

Cellulose

It is interesting that the two most well known polysaccharides have very similar units-glucose- that are connected in different geometries-one that we have the enzymes to break (starch) and the other that termites have enzymes to break (cellulose; wood)

LIPIDS/STEROIDS

Lipids are not water soluble because their overall structure is composed mainly of non-polar hydrocarbons. Fat has a glycerol that has three generally long-chained attachments forming an ester. If there is a double bond in the long-chain attachments it is referred to as **unsaturated**, and if not, it is called **saturated**. Unsaturation generally refers to as having one or more C=C double bonds or a carbon-carbon triple bonds present. A saturated compound does not have these double and triple bonds present.

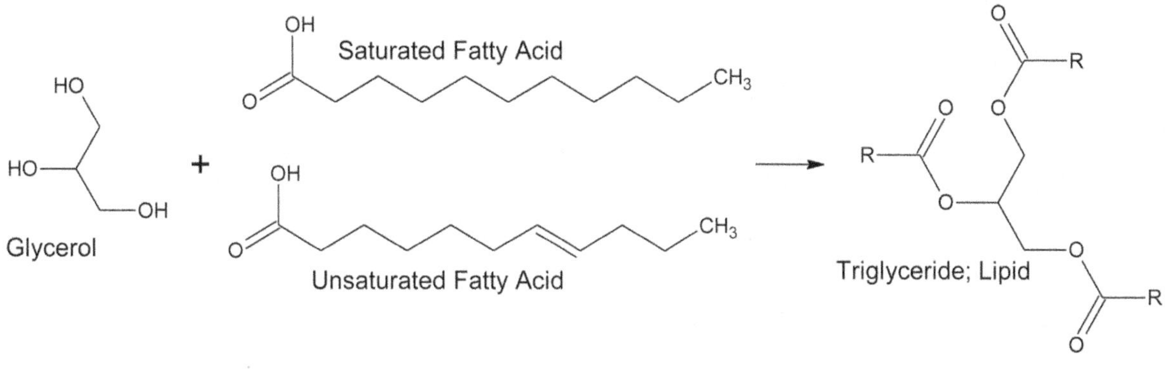

Glycerol + Saturated Fatty Acid + Unsaturated Fatty Acid → Triglyceride; Lipid

We remember that the reaction between and acid and an alcohol forms an ester. Fats are triesters or **triglycerides**, the "glyceride" name coming from the starting material glycerol. Fats are great sources of energy with 1 gram giving about 38 kJ/mol while carbohydrates give only 17 kJ/mol. The long-chained molecules are called **fatty acids**. **Unsaturated** fats are generally better for you than saturated fats. **Trans**-fats are found to be undesirable health-wise so we want unsaturated cis-fats when given the choice.

Steroids are another class of insoluble (in water) organic compounds. They have four rings connected as shown below.

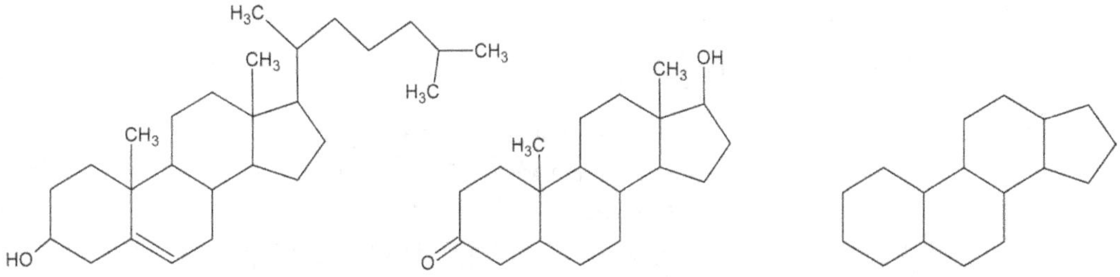

Cholesterol   Testosterone   Four connected rings

Cholesterol is a steroid as is **testosterone**. They are produced in one part of the body and influence other parts of the body.

PROTEINS

Proteins are polymers of alpha, α, amino acids. Alpha simply means substituted on the first carbon. The many different monodisperse polymers of amino acids, which are essentially components of plants and animals, are called **proteins**. This word is derived from the Greek *porteios*, "of chief importance." In proteins 20 different alpha -amino acids are joined together by peptide linkages and are also called polyamides or polypeptides. This term is often used by biologists to denote oligomers or relatively low molecular weight proteins. (Note the structural similarities and differences between proteins and polyamides-nylons.)

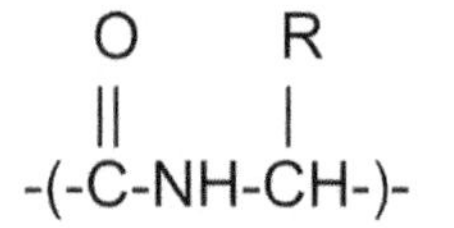

$$\begin{array}{cc} O & R \\ \| & | \\ \end{array}$$
-(-C-NH-CH-)-

All alpha-amino acids found in proteins are of the general structure

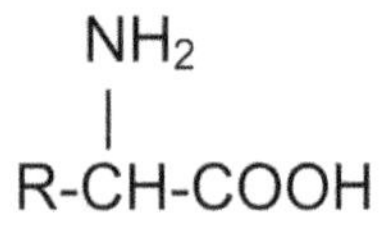

$$\begin{array}{c} NH_2 \\ | \\ \end{array}$$
R-CH-COOH

except glycine

$$\begin{array}{c} NH_2 \\ | \\ \end{array}$$
H$_2$C-COOH

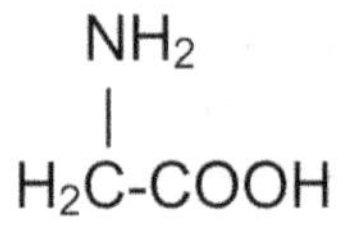

and contain a chiral carbon atom and are L-amino acids. The net ionic charge of an amino acid varies with charges in the solution pH. The pH at which an amino acid is electrically neutral is called the **isoelectric point**. For simple amino acids (containing only one acid and one amine), this occurs at a pH of about 6 with the formation of a dipolar ion or **zwitterion** as shown below.

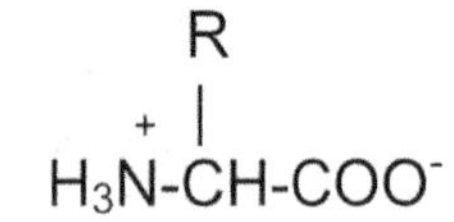

$$\begin{array}{c} R \\ + | \\ \end{array}$$
H$_3$N-CH-COO$^-$

Hence, α-amino acids, like other salts, are water-soluble, high-melting, polar compounds. As noted before, they are called alpha-amino acids because the amine and acid group are on the first or alpha carbon. Remember, that alpha is the first letter in the Greek alphabet.

In writing out sequences for polypeptides it is usual to use a three-letter abbreviation or a one letter abbreviation starting with the N-terminus to the left and going to the C-O terminus to the right. Thus the trimer

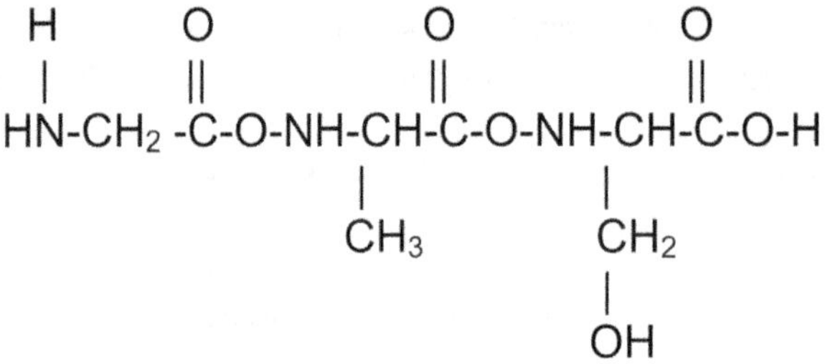

$$\begin{array}{cccc} H & O & O & O \\ | & \| & \| & \| \\ \end{array}$$
HN-CH$_2$ -C-O-NH-CH-C-O-NH-CH-C-O-H   becomes

$$\begin{array}{cc} | & | \\ CH_3 & CH_2 \\ & | \\ & OH \end{array}$$

Gly-Ala-Ser   or   GlyAlaSer or EGAS where the E signals the N-terminus or simply GAS.

It is important to remember that all proteins are polypeptides.

The amino acids may be neutral, acidic, or basic, in accordance with the relative number of amino and carboxylic acid groups present. Cations can be formed with amino acids like tryptophane, lysine, histidine, and arginine which have amine groups while others that contain acid groups can be hydrolyzed to form anions like aspartic acid and glutamic acid. The presence of varying amounts of these amino acid moieties within a protein are primary driving forces for the separation of proteins using electrophoresis and result in polypeptides having different isoelectric points. If there are a number of acidic and/or basic groups on the polypeptide the molecule is said to be a **polyampholyte** or if they contain only positive or negative charges they are called **polyelectrolytes**. The behavior of these charged polypeptides is similar to the behavior of other charged polymers. Thus, a largely hydrolyzed protein chain elongates because the negative sites repeal one another. The spacing and number of these charged sites helps determine the tertiary structure of such polypeptides.

Proteins have **primary**, simple amino acid sequence; **secondary**, coil or pleated sheet; **tertiary** structure, how the entire chain twists and turns; and **quaternary** structure, how the separate protein chains form more complex structures (myoglobin-muscle, hemoglobin-blood stream).

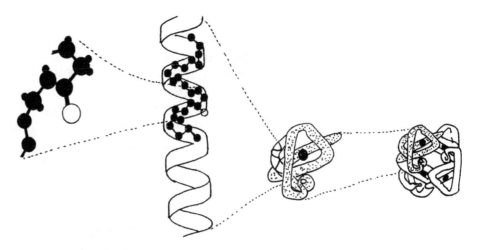

Figure 13.1 *Four levels of structure elucidation. From left to right: primary, secondary, tertiary, and quaternary structures illustrated using a globular protein segment.*

Enzymes are special generally globular proteins that perform special functions, they are nature's catalysts.

There are several models to explain the specificity of enzymes. The **lock-and-key** is one of these.

NUCLEIC ACIDS

Nucleoproteins, which are conjugated proteins, may be separated into nucleic acids and proteins. The name "nuclein," which was coined by Miescher in 1869 to describe products isolated form nuclei in pus, was later changed to nucleic acid. Somewhat pure nucleic acid was isolated by Levene in the early 1900s. He showed that either D-ribose or D-deoxyribose was present in what are now know as ribonucleic acid (RNA) and deoxyribonucleic acid (DNA). They consist of two sugars that are identical except that the deosyribose contains a hydrogen on carbon 2 (thus the name deoxy or without one "oxy" or hydroxyl) rather than a hydroxyl group. These compounds were originally obtained from yeast and the thymus gland, respectively, DNA and RNA.

Components of nucleic acids are given below and are a sugar, phosphate, and base. The sugar can be a ribose (RNA) or deoxyribose (DNA). The bases are adenine ,guanine, etc.

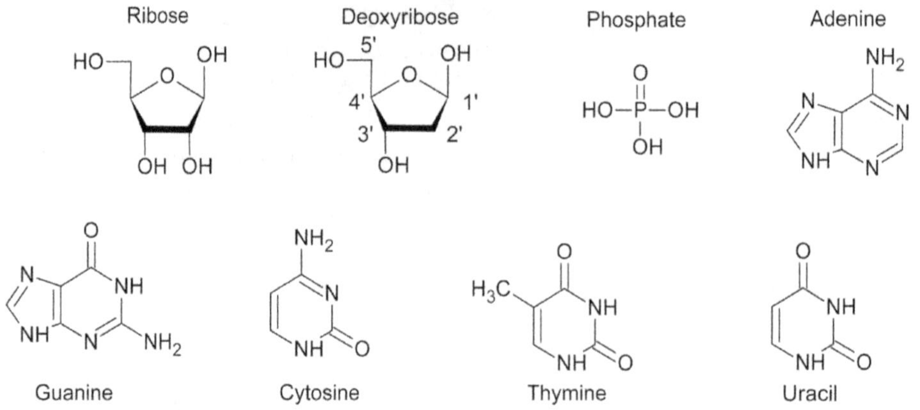

In 1944 Avery showed that DNA was able to change one strain of bacteria to another. It is now known that nucleic acids direct the synthesis of proteins. Thus, our modern knowledge of heredity and molecular biology is based on our knowledge of nucleic acids.

Recently, it was announced that the human genome was decoded. This is one of the most important events in the history of medicine and health. The human genome is composed of natures most complex, exacting, and important macromolecule. It is composed of nucleic acids that appear complex in comparison to simpler molecules such as methane and ethylene, but simple in comparison to their result on the human body. As noted before, each unit is essentially the same containing a phosphate, and a deoxyribose sugar and one of four bases with each base typically represented by the capital of the first letter of their name, G, C, A, and T. In fact, the complexity is less than having four separate and independent bases because the bases come in matched sets, they are paired. The mimetic Gee CAT allows an easy way to remember this pairing. Thus G and C couple and A and T couple. The base, sugar, and phosphate combine forming nucleotides such as adenylic acid, adenosine-3'-phosphate shown below and represented by the symbols A, dA, and dAMP.

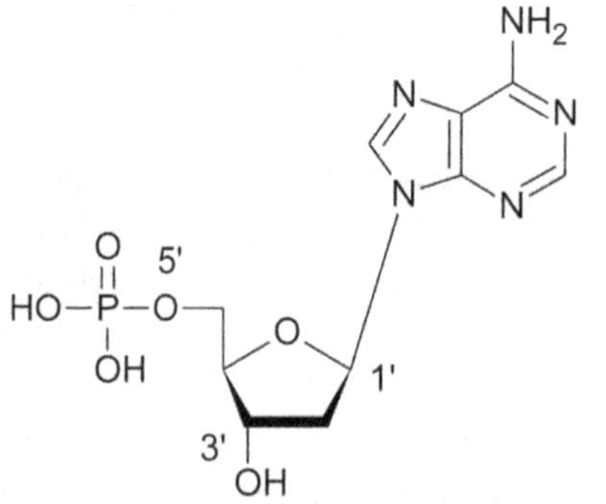

Adenylic acid, adenosine-3'-phosphate

The backbone of nucleic acids is connected through the 3' and 5' sites on the sugar with the base attached at the 1' site. Because the sugar molecule is not symmetrical each unit can be connected differently but there is order (also called sense or directionality) in the sequence of this connection so that phosphodiester linkage between units is between the 3' carbon of one unit and the 5' carbon of the next unit. Thus nucleic acids consist of units connected so that the repeat unit is a 3'–5' (by agreement we consider the start to occur at the 3' and end at the 5' though we could just as easily describe this repeat as being 5'–3') linkage. Thus, the two ends are not identical-one contains an unreacted 3' and the other an unreacted 5' hydroxyl.

A shorthand is used to describe sequences. Following is a trimer containing in order the bases cytosine, adenine, and thymine.

This sequence is described as

p-5'-C-3'-p-5'-A-3'-p-5'-T-3' or pCpApT or usually as simply CAT.

Nobel Laureates Watson and Crick correctly deduced that DNA consisted of a double-stranded helix in which a pyrimidine base on one chain or strand was hydrogen-bonded to a purine base on the other chain. The bonding distances are not the same with the GC paring more compact. This uneven pairing distances results in a DNA with a characteristic twisting giving unique structures. It is this twisting, and the particular base sequence, that eventually results in the varying chemical and subsequently biological activities for various combinations.

The glucose bonds holding the bases onto the backbone are not directly across the helix from one another. Thus, the sugar-phosphate repeat units are not the same. This dislocation creates structures referred to as major and minor grooves. It is known that at least some proteins that bind to DNA recognize the specific nucleotide sequences by "reading" the hydrogen bonding pattern presented by the edges of these grooves.

In solution, DNA is a dynamic, flexible molecule. It undergoes elastic motions on a nanosecond time scale most closely related to changes in the rotational angles of the bonds within the DNA backbone. The net result of these bendings and twistings is that DNA assumes a roughly globular or spherical tertiary shape. The overall structure of the DNA surface is not that of a reoccurring "barber pole" but rather because of the particular base sequence composition each sequence will have its own characteristic features of hills, valleys, bumps, etc.

As the two strands in a double helix separate, they act as a template for the construction of a complementary strand. This process occurs enzymatically with each nucleotide being introduced into the growing chain through matching it with its complementary base on the existing chain. Thus, two identical strands are produced when one double-helix combination replicates.

DNA chains can contain 1 million subunits with an end-to-end contour length of about 1 mm. Even with the complexity of these large macromolecules, synthesis of new chains generally occur without any change in the molecule. Even when changes occur, these giant machines have built into them "correcting" mechanisms that re-correct when mistakes occur.

Actual reproduction steps involving DNA and RNA often occur in concert with protein where the protein can act as a clamp or vice holding the various important members involved with the particular reproduction step in place. Thus, the protein complex acts as an assembly line tunnel or doughnut with the reactants present within the interior.

FLOW OF BIOLOGICAL INFORMATION

Nucleic acids, proteins, some carbohydrates and hormones are informational molecules. They carry directions for the control of biological processes. With the exception of hormones, these are macromolecules. In all these interactions, secondary forces such as hydrogen bonding and van der Waals forces, and ionic bonds and hydrophobic/hydrophilic character play critical roles. **Molecular recognition** is the term used to describe the ability of molecules to recognize and interact-bond-specifically with other molecules. This molecular recognition is based on a combination of these interactions just cited and on structure.

In general, the flow of biological information can be mapped as follows:

DNA → RNA → Protein → Cell Structure & Function

The total genetic information for each cell, called the *genome*, exists in the coded two-stranded DNA. This genetic information is **expressed** or processed either through **duplication** (**replication**) of the DNA so it can be **transferred** during cell division to a daughter cell or it can be transferred to manufactured RNA that in turn transfers the information to proteins that carry out the activities of the cell.

Duplication of double-stranded DNA is self-directed. The DNA, along with accessory proteins, directs the **replication** or construction of two complementary strands forming a new, exact replicate of the original DNA template. As each base site on the DNA becomes available through the unraveling of the double-stranded helix, a new nucleotide is brought into the process held in place by hydrogen bonding and van der Waals forces so that the bases are complementary. It is then covalently bonded through the action of an enzyme called DNA polymerase. After duplication, each DNA contains one DNA strand from the original double-stranded helix and one newly formed DNA strand. This is called *semiconservative replication* and increases the chance that if an error occurs, that the original base sequence will be retained.

How is DNA suitable as a carrier of genetic information? While we do not entirely understand several features are present in DNA. First, because of the double-stranded nature and mode of replication, retention is enhanced. Second, DNA is particularly stable within both cellular and extracellular environments, including a good stability to hydrolysis within an aqueous environment. Plant and animal DNA have survived thousands of years. Using polymerase chain reactions we can reconstruct DNA segments allowing comparisons to modern DNA.

Transcription is the term used to describe the transfer of information from the DNA to RNA. The genome is quite large, on the order of a millimeter in length if unraveled, but within it exists coding regions called genes. Transcription is similar to DNA replication except ribonucleotides are the building units instead of deoxyribonucleotides; the base thymine is replaced by uracil; the DNA:RNA duplex unravels releasing the DNA to again form its double-stranded helix with the single-stranded RNA; and the enzyme linking the ribonucleotides together is called RNA polymerase.

Many viruses and retroviruses have genomes that are single-stranded RNA instead of DNA. These include the AIDS virus and some retroviruses that cause cancer. Here, an enzyme called reverse transcriptase converts the RNA genome of the virus into the DNA of the host cell genome thus infecting the host.

The transcription of the DNA gives three kinds of RNA-ribosomal, messenger, and transfer. The most abundant RNA is ribosomal RNA, rRNA. Most rRNA is large and is found in combination with proteins in the ribonucleoprotein complexes called ribosomes. **Ribosomes** are subcellular sites for protein synthesis.

Transfer RNA, tRNA, is the smallest of the RNAs being less than 100 nucleotides long. tRNA combines with an amino acid incorporating it into a growing protein. There is at least one tRNA for each of the 20 amino acids used in protein synthesis. Messenger RNA, mRNA, is varied in size but each carries the message found in a single gene or group of genes. The sequence of bases in mRNA is complementary to the sequence of DNA bases. mRNA is unstable and short-lived so that its message for protein synthesis must be rapidly decoded. The message is decoded by the ribosomes that make several copies of the protein for each mRNA.

The ultimate purpose of DNA expression is protein synthesis. mRNA serves as the intermediate carrier of the DNA genetic information for protein synthesis. The DNA message is carried in the form of base sequences that are transferred to RNA also in terms of base sequences and finally these are transferred into amino acid sequences through a translation process based on the genetic code. This process of information from the RNA to the protein is called *translation*.

A set of coding rules are in action as in the translation process. Briefly, these are as follows. First, a set of three adjacent nucleotides compose the code for each amino acid. A single amino acid can have several **triplet codes** or *codons*. Since there are four different nucleotides (or four different bases) in DNA and RNA there exists 4^3, or 64 trinucleotide combinations. Using U as a symbol for uracil, present in RNA, the triplet or code or codon UUU is specific for phenylalanine.

Second, the code is non-overlapping so that every **three nucleotides code for an amino acid** and the next three code for a second amino acid and the third set code for a third amino acid, etc. Third, the sets of nucleotides are read sequentially without punctuation. Fourth, the code is nearly universal. Fifth, there are codes for other than amino acids but also include stop or terminate, UAG, and start or initiate, AUG.

In essence, tRNA has two active sites-one that is specific for a given amino acid and the second that is specific for a given set of three bases. The tRNA "collects" an appropriate amino acid and brings it to the growing polypeptide chain inserting it as directed by the mRNA. There is then a collinear relationship between the nucleotide base sequence of a gene and the amino acid sequence in the protein.

The amount, presence, or absence of a particular protein is generally controlled by the DNA in the cell. Protein synthesis can be signaled external to the cell or within the cell. Growth factors and hormones form part of this secondary messenger service.

The translation and transcription of DNA information is polymer synthesis and behavior and the particular governing factors and features that control these reactions are present in the synthesis and behavior of other macromolecules-synthetic and biological.

For the human genome there exists so-called coding or active regions called **exons** and noncoding regions called **introns**. The average size of an exon is about 120 to 150 nucleotide units long and for coding is about 40 to 50 amino acids. Introns vary widely in size from about 50 to over 20,000 units. About 5% of the genome is used for coding. It was thought that the other 95% was silent or junk DNA. We are finding that the intron regions play essential roles. Interestingly introns are absent in the most basic prokaryotes, only occasionally found in eukaryotes, but common in animals.

GENETIC ENGINEERING

Genetic engineering is the alteration of an organism's genetic material. The aim is to introduce into the organism's genetic material some desirable trait that is otherwise absent. Alternation of genetic material entails the use of polymer chemistry on a molecular (or nano) level making use of somewhat straightforward chemical reactions; many of the reactions employ biological entities, such as enzymes, to carry out these reactions.

Essentially, gene segments are replaced to inject into the altered microorganism genetic material that expresses the desired trait. Today, routine gene alteration is taught in undergraduate laboratories. Even so, specific gene alteration requires extensive planning and is conducted in major research laboratories.

In the broadest sense, genetic engineering refers to any artificial process that alters the genetic composition of an organism. Such alterations can be carried out indirectly through chemical methods, through radiation, or through selective breeding. Today, the term usually refers to the process whereby genes or portions of chromosomes are chemically altered.

After the alteration of a single, or few, genes, the altered genes reproduce giving much larger numbers of genes with the alternation incorporated in the their genome. The term "clone" comes from the Greek word *klon*, meaning a cutting used to propagate a plant. Cell cloning is the production of identical cells from a single cell. In like manner, gene cloning is the production of identical genes from a single gene, introduced into a host cell. Today, the term cloning refers to one special type of genetic engineering.

Genes are a chromosomal portion that codes for a single polypeptide or RNA. Gene splicing is currently practiced as the enzymatic attachment of one gene or gene segment to another gene or gene segment. Genes are composed of DNA which can be considered as a specialized polyphosphate polymer. The purpose for the manipulation of DNA can be for many reasons. One of these is the production of recombinant DNA. Here we will focus on the production of recombinant DNA. DNA cannot be directly transferred from one organism, the donor, to another recipient organism, the host. Instead, the donor DNA segment is cut and then recombined with a DNA from a host. *Escherichia coli*, *E. coli*, is typically employed as the host cell since it is itself generally a harmless bacterium that reproduces rapidly. The *E. coli* then acts as a "factory" that reproduces bacteria that contain the desired modification.

Enzymes, specialized proteins, are used as designing tools for the genetic engineering. One of these enzyme tools consists of *restriction endonucleases* that recognize specific series of base pairs. They split the DNA at these specific points. This splitting is called "lysing", which in reality is simply the hydrolysis of DNA units as shown below.

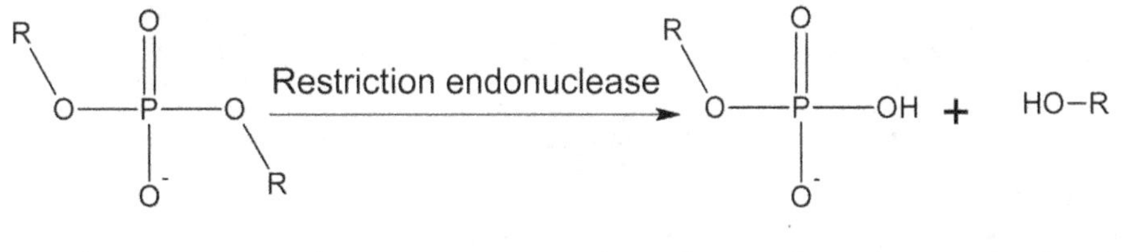

Organisms produce restriction endonucleases that are specific for that organism. Certain restriction endonucleases cut double-stranded DNA asymmetrically in regions called palindromes, that is regions that "read" (have identical sequences) the same way from left to right on one strand as right to left on the other strand. This produces what is referred to as "sticky ends" that form not only a "cleft" for attachment but also a single-stranded end that has the ability to pair with another complimentary single-stranded strand-end. Both strands of the original donor twin strand have a tendency to recombine with complementary strands of DNA from a host that has been treated to produce the complementary strands. The sticky ends, when mixed under the proper conditions in the presence of another enzyme, DNA-ligase, combine. The hydrogen bonding between complementary sticky ends re-enforce the recombination reaction. The resulting recombination reaction results in a variety of products including the desired recombination of host and donor DNA as well as the combination of the original donor strands and uncombined DNA. The mixture is often treated in one of two manners. The simplest case requires a chemical-resistant gene that is resistant to the employed chemical agent such as tetracycline. The desired recombinant genes survive and are then transferred into the host organism so the new gene can express itself.

In some cases, such as the synthesis of insulin, the recombination mixture is added to a host organism, here *E. coli*. This infected mixture is then plated out and the individual colonies tested for insulin production. Those colonies that produce insulin are further platted out and grown for mass insulin production. Cells that accept the recombinant DNA are called **transformed**. More specialized sequences have been developed to increase the probability of gene incorporation and its successful reproduction.

A second tool employed by the genetic engineer is the enzyme terminal transferase that adds deoxyribonuclease resides to the 3′ end of DNA strands creating 3′ tails of a single type of residue.

Special modified plasmid DNA's, called **vectors** or carriers, are used as host or targets for gene modification. These circularly shaped vectors reproduce autonomously in host cells. Plasmids have two other important properties. First, they can pass from one cell to another allowing a single "modified" bacterial cell to inject neighboring bacterial cells with this "modification." Second, gene material from other cells can be easily formed into plasmids, allowing ready construction of modified carriers.

The steps involved in gene splicing, emphasizing the chemical nature of the individual steps, are as follows:

1. Lysing, which is really simply the hydrolysis of DNA units as shown above.

2. Construction of staggered, sticky, ends.

3. Recombination or lysation, the reverse of lysing, chemically formation of a phosphate ester as below connecting the desired segment to the DNA of the host cell.

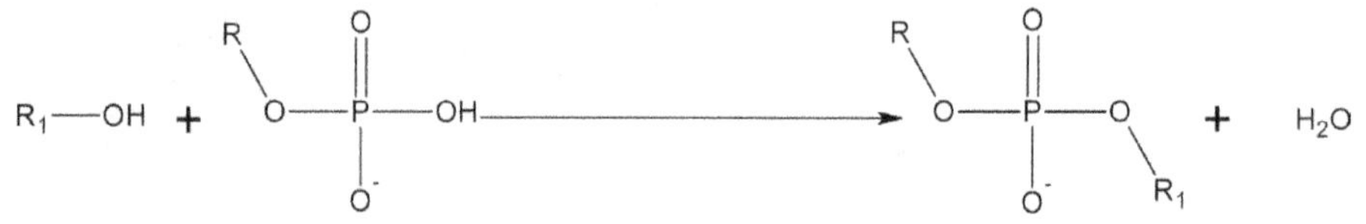

4. Chemical recombination of vector-insertion into the host cell; recombining plasmid genes into the host genetic complement.

5. Replication of host cell.

There are many uses of recombinant DNA. As noted above, one technique that produces recombinant DNA is called cloning. In one cloning technique used for the production of the sheep Dolly in 1996, the DNA nucleus from a female's egg is replaced with a nucleus from another sheep. The egg is placed in the uterus of a third animal, known as the surrogate mother. Dolly is nearly genetically identical to the animal from which the nucleus was obtained but not genetically related to the surrogate mother.

Recombinant DNA has been used in a variety of ways. The growth hormone gene of rainbow trout has been transferred into carp eggs resulting in the transgenic carp producing larger fish. The milk product of dairy cows has been increased by cloning and introducing into the cows the cattle growth hormone bovine somatotropin.

Transgenic strawberry and potato plants have been produced that are frost-resistant. Cotton, corn, soybean plants have been produced with increased resistance to herbicides allowing herbicide use without killing the transgenic crop-producing plants. Larger and smaller varieties of other food-producing plants have been produced using recombinant DNA giving plants that produce certain amino acids needed for our nutrition.

Transgenic bacteria have been produced that can metabolize petroleum products including certain synthetic polymers.

Along with the production of insulin, many other medical uses have been achieved for recombinant DNA. This includes the production of *erythropoietin*, a hormone used to stimulate production of red blood cells in anemic people; tissue *plasminogen activator* an enzyme that dissolves blood clots in heart attack victims; and *antihemophillic human factor VIII*, used to prevent and control bleeding for people with hemophilia. These three important genetically engineered proteins were all cloned in hamster cell cultures.

Gene engineering is the basis of gene therapy where genes are removed, replaced, or altered producing new proteins for the treatment of such diseases as muscular dystrophy, some cancers, adenosine deaminase deficiency, cystic fibrosis, and emphysema.

DNA PROFILING

DNA profiling is also referred to as DNA fingerprinting and DNA typing. It is used in paternity identification, classification of plants, criminal cases, identification of victims, heredity (of living, recently deceased, and anciently deceased), etc. DNA profiling is a tool that allows a comparison of DNA samples.

While about 99.9% of our DNA is alike, the 0.1 % is what makes us individuals, and it is this 0.1 % that allows for the identification of us as individuals. Of interest, it is not within the gene portions that makeup our different physical and mental characteristics, but DNA profiling employs DNA taken from what is referred to as the "junk DNA." Identification generally occurs because of the formation of different lengths of this junk DNA after appropriate treatment. This junk DNA contains the same sequence of base pairs, but in different repeat numbers. Thus, the sequence ATTCGG may appear four times, five times, six times, etc. There are typically some statistical number of repeats. Other sequences such as GGCATCC and AATGCAAT also appear in some statistical number of repeats. While each of us have these different run sequences, individually we have unique run lengths of these different run sequences. These run sequences are called variable number of tandem repeats or VNTRs. The repeat runs used for identification are generally from specific locations within a chromosome. Enzymes "cut" the associated DNA at specific locations leading to decreases in DNA molecular weight. In fact, these DNA chain length decreases are apparent as bandshifts in DNA gels. The combination of the differences in decreased DNA chain lengths becomes unique as results are obtained from different enzymes are accumulated. These changes in the movement of DNA segments are then compared with results from different individuals and identification as to whether the tested individuals are the same or different. The identity results are often given as some percentage or ratio.

There are two basic types of DNA profiling; one that uses polymerase chain reaction (PCR) enzymes and the second employs the restriction fragment length polymorphism (RFLP) enzymes. The PCR approach utilizes a sort of molecular copying process where a specific region is selected for investigation. The PCR approach requires only a few nanograms of DNA. The DNA polymerase makes copies of DNA strands in a process that mimics the way DNA replicates naturally within the cell. Segments are selected for special study and the results used to identify the DNA pattern.

With the exception of identical twins, each individual has a DNA profile that is unique. As previously noted, in excess of 99.9% of the over 3 billion nucleotides in human DNA are the same. But, for every 1000 nucleotides there is an average of one site of variation or polymorphism. These DNA polymorphisms change the length of the DNA fragments produced by certain restriction enzymes. The resulting fragments are called restriction fragments length polymorphisms, or RFLP's. Gel electrophoresis is typically employed to separate the sizes and thus create a pattern of RFLLP's. The number and size of the fragments is used to create the DNA profile.

Several steps are involved in creating the genetic fingerprint. First, a sample of cells is obtained from a person's blood, bone, semen, hair roots, or saliva. The individual cells from the sample are split open and DNA isolated. The DNA is treated with restriction enzymes that cleave the DNA strands at specific locations creating fragments of varying lengths and composition. The resulting fragments undergo electrophoresis using a gel which allows the separation of the fragmented DNA. Because the gel is fragile, a thin nylon membrane, covered by a towel, is laid over the gel. As moisture is drawn to the towel from the electrophoresis gel, the DNA fragments are transferred to the nylon membrane. This process is called blotting. The DNA bands are visible to the eye but they are too numerous to be useful. Thus, a radioactive solution is washed over the nylon membrane that binds to like fragments, generally to only 6 to 20 of the DNA clusters. A sheet of photographic film is placed on top of the nylon membrane that records these cluster sites. The film is then developed producing a pattern of thick-and-thin bands. This pattern is the genetic pattern for that particular sample. This process can take a month or more at commercial labs for routine analysis, but when needed, the analysis can be made in only a day or two.

There are different restriction enzymes that cut DNA at different sites. The previous sequence can be repeated several times for the same DNA sample. From a study of each restriction enzyme, a probability that another person will have the same profile is assigned. Thus, one restriction enzyme may have the possibility that another person has the same match of 1 in 100 or 1%. A second restriction enzyme may have the probability of 1 in 1000 or 0.1%. A third restriction enzyme may have a probability for a match being 1 in 500 or 0.2%. If there is a match with all three restriction enzymes, the probability would be $0.01 \times 0.001 \times 0.002$ or 0.00000002 or 0.000002% or 1 part in 50,000,000. There is a caution to using the "multiplication rule," in that DNA sequences are not totally random. In fact, DNA sequence agreements generally diverge as one's ancestors are less closely related.

The RFLP method requires a sample about 100 times larger than required for the PCR approach, but with repeated sequences using different restriction enzymes, RFLP is more precise.

It must be noted that factors leading to DNA degradation, such as moisture, chemicals, bacteria, heat, and sunlight will impact negatively on

DNA profiling since the precise sequences and length of the DNA and DNA fragments may be changed. While DNA, in general, is robust and can exist "alive" over thousands of years (such as the germination of seeds found in the pyramids of Egypt), DNA degradation decreases the probability of precise matches. Also, DNA contamination by addition of DNA from another source greatly confuses the final results.

DNA sequencing has found importance in a wide range of areas. It is being used to identify individuals at greater risk for having certain diseases such as breast cancer. It is used for the screening of certain diseases such as the presence of the sickle-cell gene.

The initial VNTRs were several hundred nucleotide units long requiring long lab periods for the various segments to separate on the gel. Today, most tests employ shorter, 3 to 5 nucleotides long, VNTRs that allow for more rapid movement on the gel resulting in faster and less costly results. It also allows for the production of a greater number of sequences that are looked at and hence, a greater ability to match/not match the results. These shorter sequences are called short tandem repeats, STRs.

While DNA is more robust than often depicted in movies, age and extreme conditions such as a fire can substantially degrade it. In such cases mitochondrial DNA is best used. Unlike nuclear DNA, mitochondrial genome exists in thousands of copies and is less apt to degrade and it is inherited only from the mother. Here, STRs are not analyzed, but rather the focus is on variable regions of the mitochondrial genome. Such analyses take much longer but are used for situations where time is not essential.

This type of DNA profiling has allowed taxonomists to determine evolutionary relationships among plants, animals, and other life forms. Currently it is a basis for the so-called Eve theory that says all of us are related to a common woman, called Eve after the Biblical Eve. It is also being used to trace the (ancient) movement of people about Earth.

DNA profiling was used to determine whether bones unearthed that were said to be from Jesse James were in fact his. DNA samples were taken from grandchildren and compared to those obtained from the bone material and shown to be similar, so that while it cannot be absolutely said the bones were from Jesse James, DNA evidence was consistent with them being his bones. DNA profiling has also been used in the identification of 9/11 victims, and a number of mass graves throughout the world.

In 1998 the Combined DNA Index System, CODIS, system was begun by the FBI. It is an automated forensic data bank and contains DNA profile data related to most of the recent major crimes. It is also connected with state systems as well as similar world-wide data bases.

VITAMINS/MINERALS & FOOD

Vitamins are organic and minerals are inorganic. Both are essential to our health. Linus Pauling was the first to promote the taking of vitamins arguing that when the body is building various needed proteins, nucleic acids, cells, etc. that it was more likely that the correct structure would be build if the body had available to itself the needed building blocks rather than having to synthesize them.

Metabolism is the use or incorporation of building blocks into our human body to make the cells, nucleic acids, muscles, skin, hair, heart, teeth, etc. **Catabolism** involves the tearing-down of biomolecules-digestion and cellular respiration are examples. **Anabolism** is somewhat the opposite- it involves the building up of large biomacromolecules from smaller molecules. These two work together- building blocks and energy from one contributes to the other.

We are what we eat, or something like that. **Lipoproteins** are water soluble lipid- protein materials. *Very-low-density lipoproteins* (VLDL) serve primarily in the transport of fats; **Low-density lipoproteins** (LDL) transport cholesterol to the cells, where it is used to build cell walls. **High-density lipoproteins** (HDL) bring cholesterol to the liver where it is transformed into a number of useful biomolecules. Fatty deposits are formed on the inner wall of arteries and are encouraged by a diet high in saturated fats that leads to high levels of VLDL and LDL. Unsaturated fats tend to increase blood HDL and removal of plaque. Unsaturated fats are transformed into saturated fats through hydrogenation to the double bonds, sites of unsaturation.

Essential amino acids are amino acids that are needed by the body but not made by our bodies. There are 8 essential amino acids for grownups and 10 for children.

Carbohydrates can be divided into two groups- nondigestible (dietary fiber) and digestible (food, starches and sugars). Dietary fiber helps intestine movement of food-type materials. Digestible foods can be rated according to how fast they give increases in the blood glucose levels (glycemic index). While the rate at which foods increase the blood glucose levels varies from person to person and from food to food, the glycemic index is one indicator. Thus, a runner or a diabatic may want to control their level and can use this index as a ball-park value.

CAUTIONS

As we look at the topics of energy, resources, air, global warming, etc. we might remember the following.

Our earth is a dynamic equilibrium system or in reality, a very complex of interlocking equilibrium systems. Devolving is natural and there is little we can do about it. Entropy, randomness, increases. That is one of the laws of thermodynamics and we see it occurring all about us. Water and air are leaving Earth to outer space. But, there are aspects of this quasi-equilibrium system that we can influence, at least as far as how fast it is moving from a desired equilibrium position to an undesirable equilibrium point. This includes the atmosphere, water, land, and food. All of these are interrelated. Another aspect is the time constant related to moving from one equilibrium position to moving to another equilibrium position. Often this time constant is long. (It takes decades to influence the ozone layer and many more to allow it to replenish itself.) We can get some idea as to the approach to another equilibrium position once equilibrium is upset by looking at a pendulum and seeing how long it takes for the pendulum to come to rest once it is disturbed. This is a good analogy as nature opposes changes attempting to move the pendulum back towards the "original" (Le Chatelier's principle) equilibrium (resting) position. Another idea, is that once we interact with some natural setting, such as a forest, can we retrieve it to its precise "pre-interaction" setting. The answer is "no." We can approximate movement back to what it once was, but we will not truly reach back to its pre-disturbed setting once we have impacted the forest area.

Be aware of who is giving you information and why. Be skeptical and armed (educated). Most of our current environmental concerns have both political and monetary aspects. There will be "hidden agendas", unintended consequences, opposing arguments and information, etc. Most arguments will be set so that the conclusion must be "either this" or "that" as the solution. This is like asking whether a wall is black or white. The wall may be blue, or brown, multicolored, or etc. Thus, look for answers that allow both (several) deserving solutions to occur. Look for alternatives. Also, remember that the rest of the world is not in your situation and may have needs that are unlike yours.

Drugs

INTRODUCTION

Drugs are any substance (not food or water) that affects how our body functions. Drugs are controlled by a number of agencies and laws. The father of toxicology said that everything can be toxic- it depends on the amount and location. What does this mean? What is the difference between legal and illegal drugs? Drugs with therapeutic value are called **medicines**.

The US Drug Enforcement Agency (DEA) classifies drugs as follows:

Over-the-counter	Available to all	Aspirin
Permitted nonmedical drugs	Available in foods, etc.	Alcohol, cigarettes, Caffeine
Prescription	Requires doctors OK	Cipro
Controlled substances		
Schedule 1 No medical use, high abuse		LSD, heroin
Schedule 2 Some medical use, high abuse		Marijuana, codeine
Schedule 3 Prescription, abuse possible		Valium

Drugs include both natural (caffeine, penicillin, taxol) and synthetic (LSD, ciprofloxacin, cisplatin) drugs.

It is note worthy that drug doses generally come in a limited number of choices. For instance, many generally come in only three tablet sizes- 250, 500, and 750 mg. It is up to the physician to prescribe which dosage is best and the frequency and duration that the drug is to be taken. These dosage sizes are intended to reflect an average person. Because we have different metabolic rates and efficiencies with respect to drug action as well as different body weights and health parameters each of us require different doses to give the desired effect. Unfortunately, the precise dose necessarily to treat a specific illness for a specific person is not known and only a limited dose sizes are economically feasible. Thus, the prescribed dose is often an educated guess by the physician.

Most drugs have a combination of hydrophobic (meaning water hating) and hydrophilic (water loving) sites. Look for these combinations in the drugs pictured in this section. The hydrophobic sites are non-polar with high hydrocarbon contents. The hydrophilic sites are polar and have such functional groups as carbonyls, amines, alcohols, esters, ethers, and amides present. This combination allows the drugs to be partially compatible with the largely water-world of the body as well as being able to pass into and out of the non-polar cell walls if needed.

As noted before, all drugs are toxic to one extent or another. Toxicity involves the affect of various materials on living objects including bacteria, plants, mice, fish, and humans. Tests to determine the toxicity of materials are typically done in a number of ways including inhalation, simple skin contact, and injection under the skin.

While mainly concerned with the affects of various agents on humans, most standard tests are carried out on animals, often a suitable test animal that is believed to be a good model for transferring results from the animal tests to humans. Table 14.1 contains some of the toxicity values found in today's literature.

Table 14.1 *Descriptions of Toxic Measures*

TDLo/Tpxic Dose Low- The lowest dose introduced by any route other than inhalation over any period of time that produces any toxic effect in humans or to produce carcinogenic, teratogenic, mutagenic, or neoplastic effects in humans and animals.

TCLo/Toxic Concentration Low- Any concentration in air that causes any toxic effect in humans or produces a carcinogenic, teratogenic, mutagenic, or neoplastigenic toxic effect in humans or animals.

LDLo/Lethal Dose Low- The lowest dose introduced by any route other than by inhalation over a time to have caused death in humans or the lowest single dose to have caused death in animals.

LD_{50}/Lethal Dose Fifty- A calculated dose expected to cause the death of 50% of a tested population from exposure by any route other than inhalation.

LCLo/Lethal Concentration Low- The lowest concentration in air to have caused death in a human or animal when exposed for 24 hours or less.

LC_{50}/Lethal Concentration Fifty- A calculated concentration of a substance in air that would cause death in 50% of a test population from exposure for 24 hours or less.

EEGL/Emergency Exposure Guideline Level-Exposure limits for very short exposure.

WEEL/Workplace Environmental Exposure Level- Exposure limits for healthy workers exposed repeatedly without adverse health effects.

OEL/Occupational Exposure Limits- Worker exposure guide.

PREL/Permissible Exposure Limits- Worker exposure limits for no ill effect.

NOAEL/No Observable Adverse Effect Level- Safe usage level.

LOAEL/Lowest Observable Adverse Effect Level- Safe usage level.

Figure 14.1 *Disease tendency chart.*

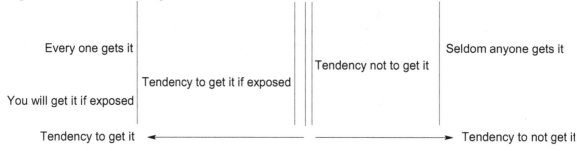

The **Placebo effect** is where a person feels a reduction in pain though given only a sugar or other tablet. Endorphins are believed to be involved and are activated by the brain in response to a positive feeling that they have received a real drug that is helping them. This is an important aspect in evaluating drug testing results.

PAIN CONTROL

Today, one of the areas where much research is needed is pain control. Pain control is needed for both those in constant pain but where the cause is not life-threatening and in situations where the patient is near death such as in the last stages of cancer. **Morphine** is often given to terminal patients for pain control but it also deadens the thought processes so many patients chose to spend their last days in pain with a somewhat clear mind.

Most drug design today is based on locating an active site and trying to occupy it with a look-alike that will keep the site occupied. This "look-alike" approach is also called the "**lock-and-key model**." Thus, morphine-like drugs generally all have the same fused ring system:

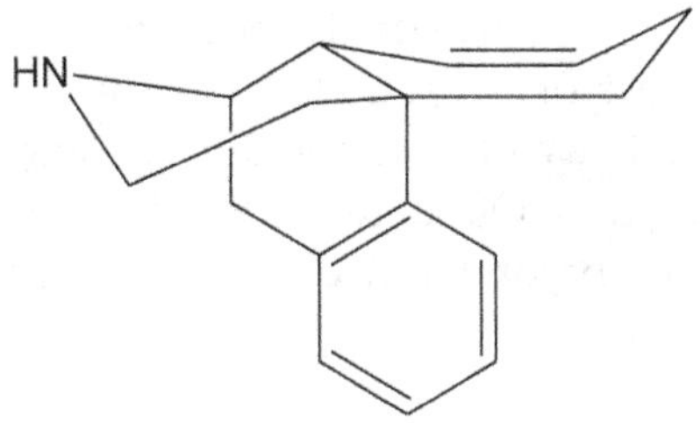

General Structure

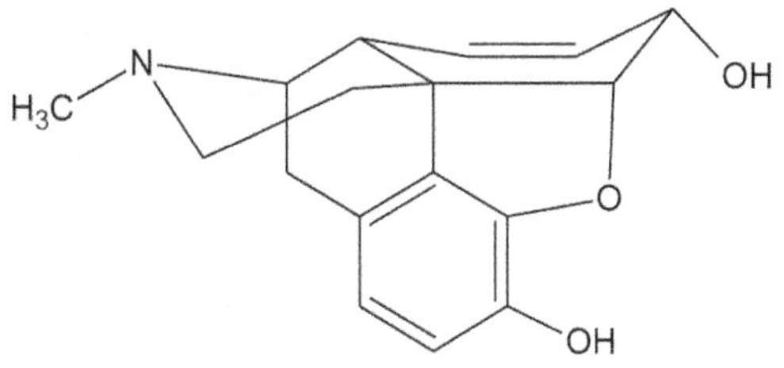

Morphine

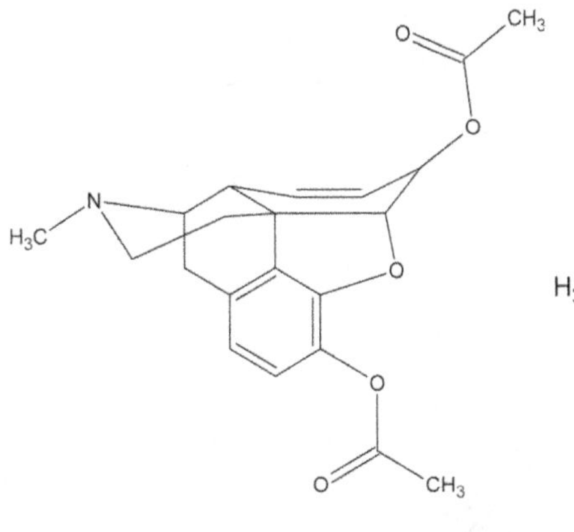

Heroin

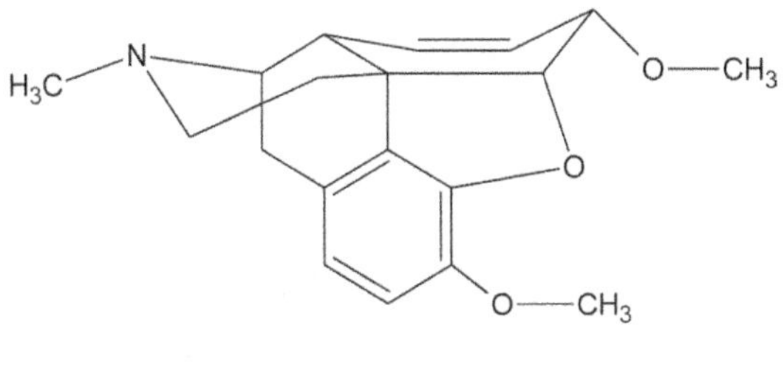

Codeine

The potent opium-like drugs described here act to inhibit our perception of pain through binding to neuron receptor sites. **Meperidine** (Demerol) and **fentanyl** (Sublimaze) are two synthetic narcotics used to assist in pain control and they are also used in low concentrations to control nerves and in other medical uses.

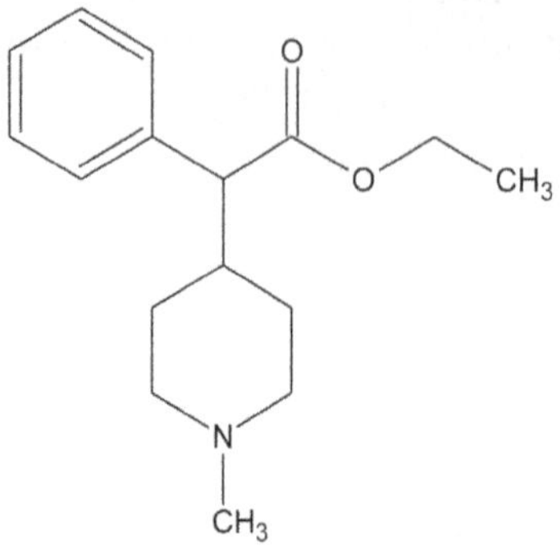

Meperidine (Demerol) 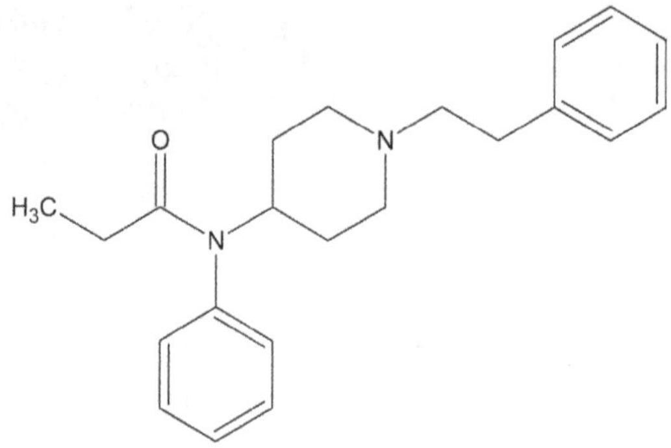   Fentanyl (Sublimaze)

There are two general types of drugs that inhibit the transmission or perception of pain. Anesthetics stop neutrons from transmitting sensations to our brain. Local anesthetics such as **procaine** (Novocain) are injected to dull or stop pain. There are a wide variety of such local anesthetics with most of them having some structural similarities. These structural similarities are the presence of an aromatic ring linked to an amine group which is in turn connected to a carbonyl-containing moiety and finally again another amine-containing unit. Of interest is that **benzocaine** does not have this second amine-containing unit and, in fact, it is only mildly effective at controlling pain.

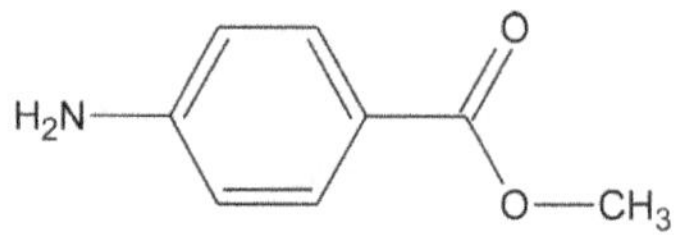

Benzocaine

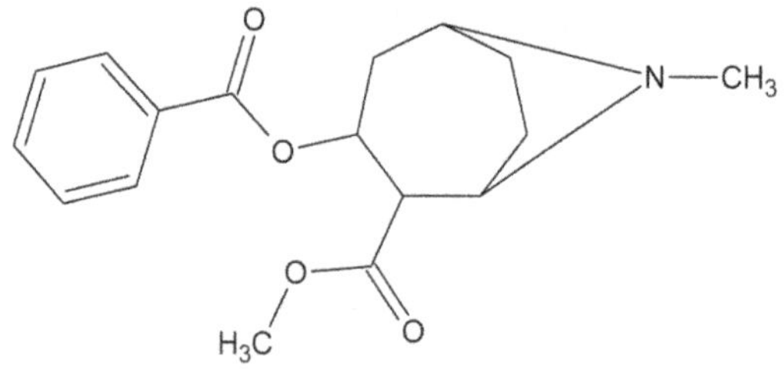

Cocaine

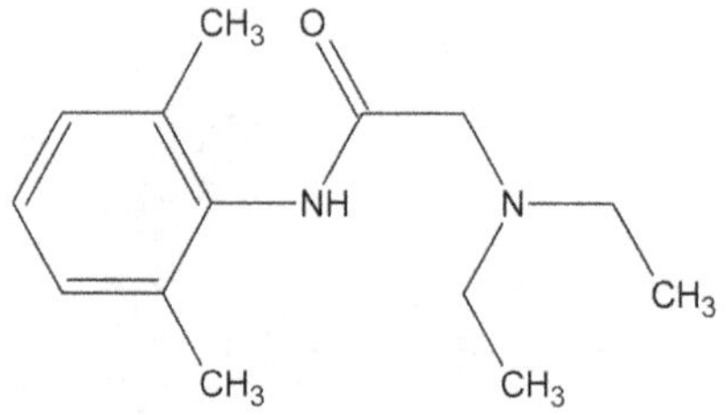

Lidocaine (Xylocaine)

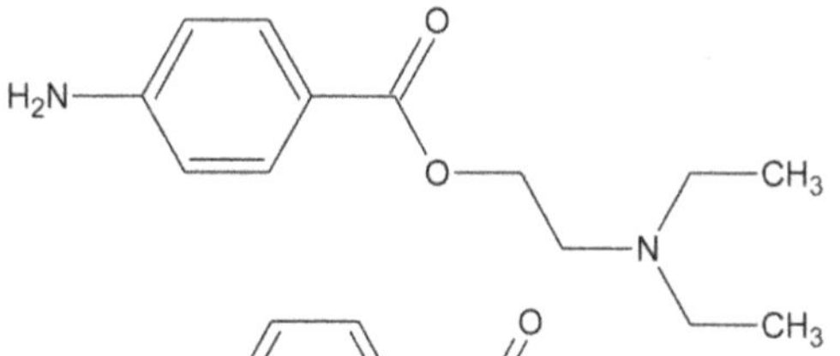

Procaine (Novocaine)

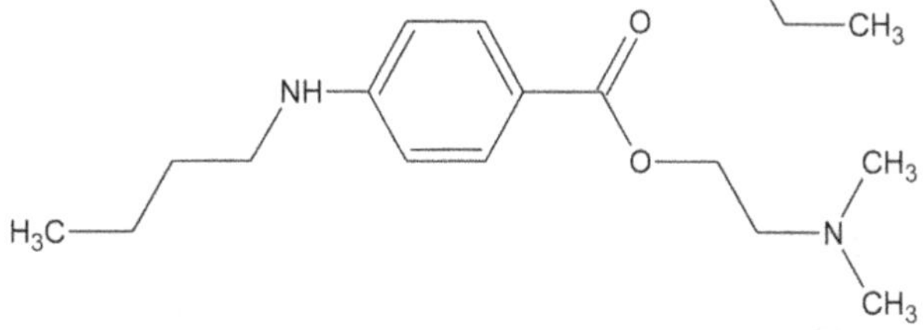

Tetracaine

There are a number of general or entire body anesthetics that block out pain by rendering us unconscious. Most of these are gases because they allow the anesthesiologist good control of the amount of anesthetic used to control the patients awareness. The first widespread synthetic entire anesthetic was **ether**, or more properly described as **diethyl ether**. Because of the explosiveness of diethyl ether when in the presence of a spark, explosions involving patients, physicians, and hospital rooms were an occasional consequence. Physicians started to wear rubber soled shoes to cut down on the incidence of such sparks. Today there exist a wide variety of other less flammable general anesthetics including a group of halo anesthetics such as **servoflurane**.

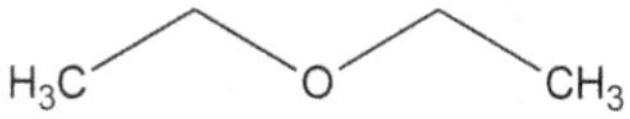

Diethyl ether 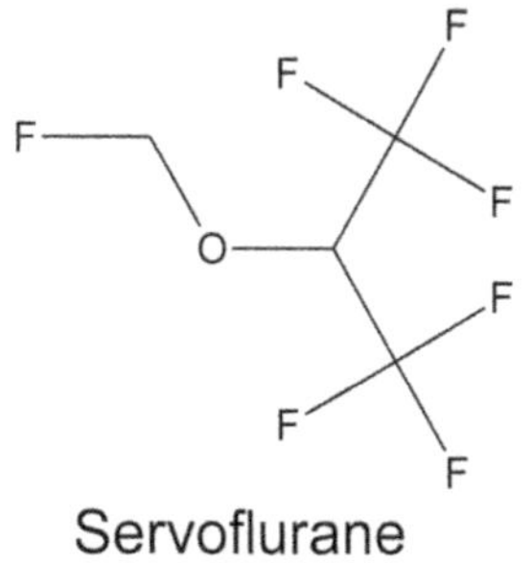   Servoflurane

Analgesics are drugs that increase our ability to withstand pain without particularly inhibiting nerve function. Many over-the-counter analgesics inhibit the synthesis of prostaglandin. In essence, **arachidonic acid**, which is formed from such traumatic events as the rupturing of the plasma membrane by a sharp object like a nail, normally enters the appropriate receptor site and is converted into prostaglandin. Because these receptor sites are already occupied by the analgesic drug, prostaglandin production is inhibited cutting down on its ability to act as a pain messenger. **Prostaglandins** also increase body temperature. Thus, their reduction reduces the amount of pain messengers and body temperature.

Arachidonic Acid   Prostaglandin

Over-the-counter analgesics include **aspirin**, the most widely used drug, as well as **ibuprofen** (Advil, Motrin), **acetaminophen** (Datril, Tylenol), and **naproxen** (Aleve).

Aspirin   Naproxen

Ibuprofen   Acetaminophen

STIMULANTS

There are a number of "legal" stimulants. The main ones are caffeine and nicotine. An average cup of coffee contains between 50 to 150 mg of caffeine; cola drinks contain about 50 mg; a single NO Doz pill contains 100 mg of caffeine.

As the **caffeine** drink is consumed, caffeine enters the bloodstream. It interacts with nerve cells blocking adenosine receptors. Under normal conditions adenosine binds to these receptors suppressing the outflow of neurotransmitters, especially dopamine and norepinephrine. By blocking these receptors, caffeine causes increased levels of dopamine and norepinephrine resulting in the person feeling alert, awake, and competent as well as a feeling that sleep is not needed. It is of interest that high doses, 1 to 2 grams (10 to 20 cups of coffee) produce anxiety, agitation, tremors, and insomnia. Ten grams of caffeine causes death.

Caffeine   Nicotine

Nicotine is found in cigarette smoke, chewing tobacco, nicotine skin patches, and nicotine gum. It is readily absorbed through the skin including the mouth, and in the lungs entering the blood stream. In the bloodstream it interacts with acetylcholine receptors in the central nervous system activating these receptors increasing the heart rate and blood pressure. This in turn releases adrenaline resulting in general feelings of being alert and attentive. This also triggers a cyclic progression where the person's body signals that they must continue to get nicotine to avoid withdrawal effects which can include restlessness, insomnia, anxiety, and anger. Smokers generally experience some withdrawal symptoms in the morning since they have gone without the nicotine "hit" for 6 to 8 hours. The results of smoking have been well documented with increased lung cancer, emphysema, mouth and throat cancer, bronchitis, and cardiovascular problems. On the average, each cigarette shortens the life of the smoker by about 15 mins. It also shortens the life expectancy of those breathing so called "second hand smoke."

DRUGS THAT TRANQUILIZE

There are a number of drugs that are depressants that dull the central nervous system. As with most drugs, the effects are concentration or dose related. At low dosages, depressants act to make a person "mild" or to "chill out" reducing their anxiety level allowing them to "unwind." At higher levels they can produce sedation, coma, and eventually death. Included as tranquilizers are benzodiazepines, barbiturates and ethanol.

Barbiturates have been used from about the 1910s through the 1960s to treat insomnia and anxiety. Drugs can have cumulative effects that are dangerous. Thus, many barbiturates taken with alcohol intensify the effect of both of the drugs and can lead to coma and death. Two of the common barbiturates are **barbital** and **phenobarbital**.

Phenobarbital   Barbital

By the 1970s barbiturates were replaced with benzodiazepines such as **chlordiazepoxide** (Librium) and **diazepam** (Valium). They are less additive in comparison to the barbiturates. Today, there is a variety of other sleep-aids such as **zolpidem** and **melatonin** and anxiety treatments including a wide variety of natural remedies. Many commercial drugs are sold under a variety of tradenames. Thus, zolpidem is sold under such trade names as Ambien, Stilnox, Hypnogen, Zolt, Stilnoct, Zolfresh, Myslee, Sanval, and Nimadorm. Often these tradenames attempt to convey the use of the drug such as Myslee has many of the letters of "sleep" within it and Zolfresh has the word "fresh" within it. Many of these drugs come in a variety of packaging including control release formulations that act to lengthen the time that the optimum dose is present.

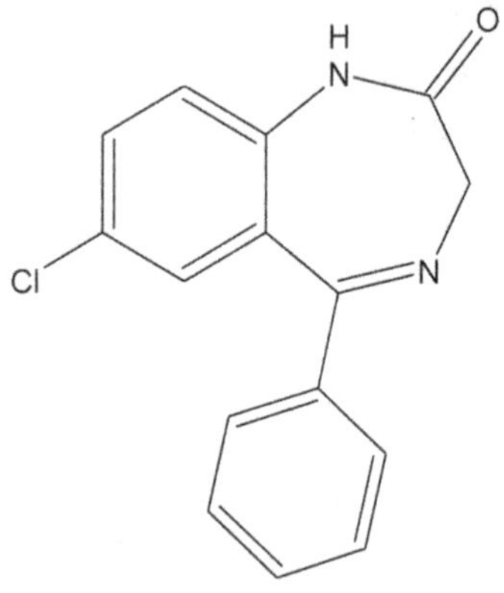

Diazepam

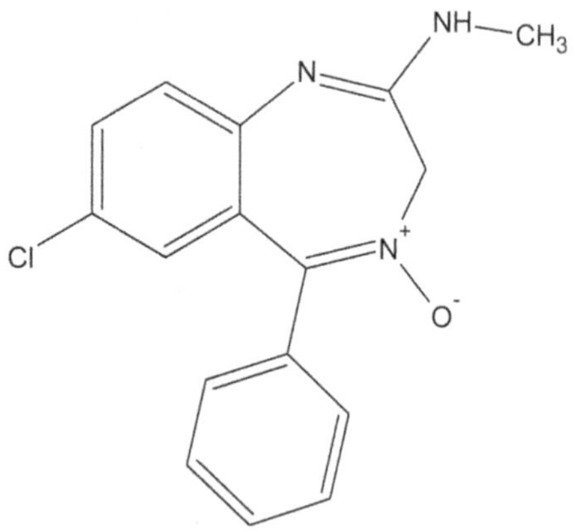

Chlordiazepoxide

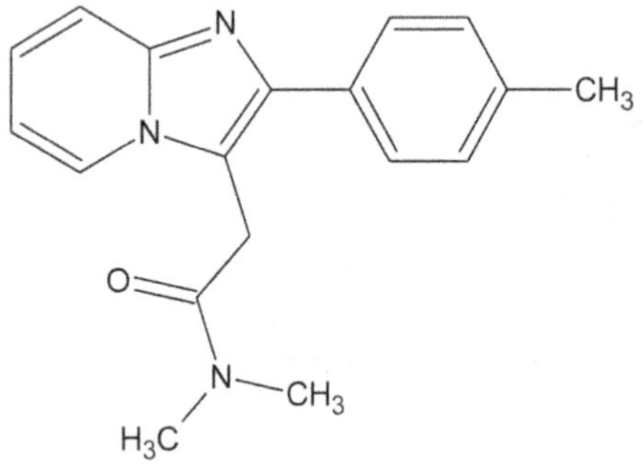

Zolpidem

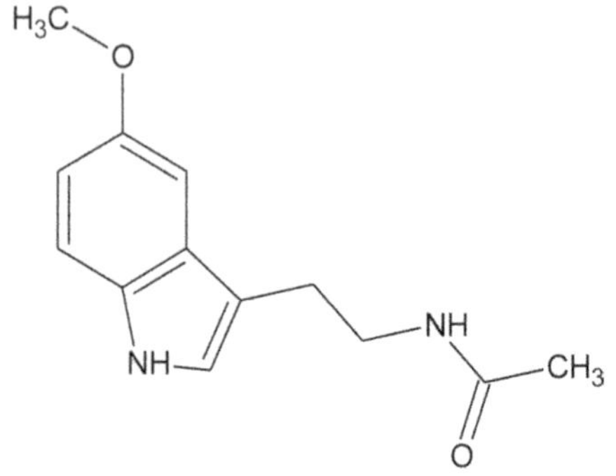

Melatonin

The most common depressant is known as **alcohol**, or more properly ethyl alcohol or **ethanol**. In comparison to most other alcohols, ethanol is less toxic. It is one of the oldest drugs used by humans prepared from the fermentation of most carbohydrates including grapes and other fruits. From starch the sequence is starch → maltose → glucose → to ethanol. As little as two beers is believed to impair a person's ability to drive a car. Table 14.2

contains the general relationship between amount of alcohol consumed and impairment. For comparison, two whiskey shots, about 30 mL each, gives a person about a blood alcohol content of 0.05%.

Table 14.2 *Toxic effects of ethanol in humans.*

Alcohol content (%-in blood)	Effect
0.01–0.05	Reflexes slowed
0.05–0.15	Coordination impaired
0.15–0.20	Intoxication
0.30–0.40	Unconsciousness
> 0.5	Possible death

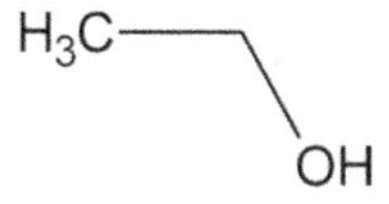

Ethanol

As noted above, some drugs act to intensify the actions of the combined drugs. Thus, the combination of ethanol and nicotine increases the incidence of throat cancer by many times because the alcohol "washes" away the protective mucus layer in the throat exposing the throat directly to the nicotine.

MIND-ALTERING DRUGS

Mind-altering drugs have been used for thousands of years as a part of religious rites. **Mescaline**, obtained from the peyote cactus, has been used by American Indians for several thousand years. When orally taken it is quickly absorbed into the blood stream where it interacts with nerve cells. In general, nerve cells are bombarded by lots of signals that it is able to filter out. These filtered out noises include the ticking of a clock or creaks in a house. Such noises, while heard, are filtered out as being insignificant. Many hallucinogenic drugs suppress this filtering process making the person aware of the once filtered noises with a subsequent distortion of reality.

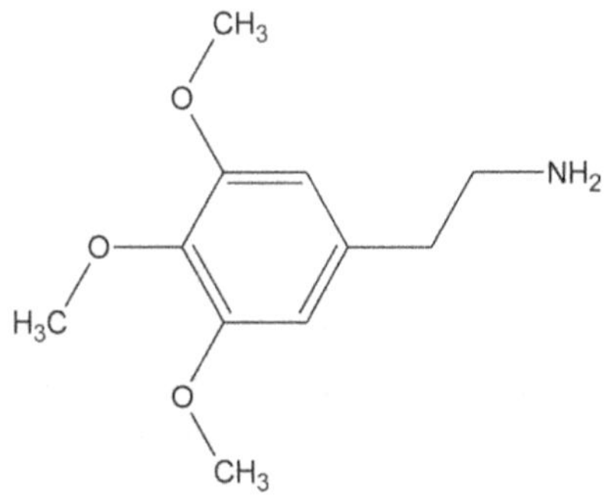

Mescaline

In large doses it promotes time distortion, altered color and sound perception, dreams, and the feeling of being separated.

Today, there exist a number of other drugs that produce similar results. Lysergic acid, **LSD**, was initially synthesized by Abbe Hoffman in 1938. After some experimentation he became "turned on" and worked to have others "turned on" with him. LSD is a much stronger hallucinogen and less powerful stimulate compared to mescaline. **MDMS** is a current designer drug sold on the streets under the name "ecstasy." Most of the hallucinogenic drugs are addictive and generally produce long term metal problems.

LSD, Lysergic Acid   MDMA

Marijuana comes from the weed plant *Cannabis sativa*. The active ingredient is Δ -9-tetrahydrocannabinol, THC. The percentage of THC varies widely in plants and locations. Marijuana changes nerve signals producing a sedative and mild hallucinogenic effect. In low doses it acts to relax a person including a feeling of well-being. At high doses it produces depression and panic reactions. It is believed that THC produces changes in the chromosomes that are passed on to children.

THC

Today, there are a number of drugs produced to treat anxiety. Valium has become a common word in today's language of drugs. Today, there are other similar drugs that specifically target serotonin-specific anti-depression. These include **sertraline** (Zoloft), and **fluoxetine** (Prozac), and paxil. Unlike valium that had a noticeable sedative effect, Prozac treats depression without the sedative side-effects.

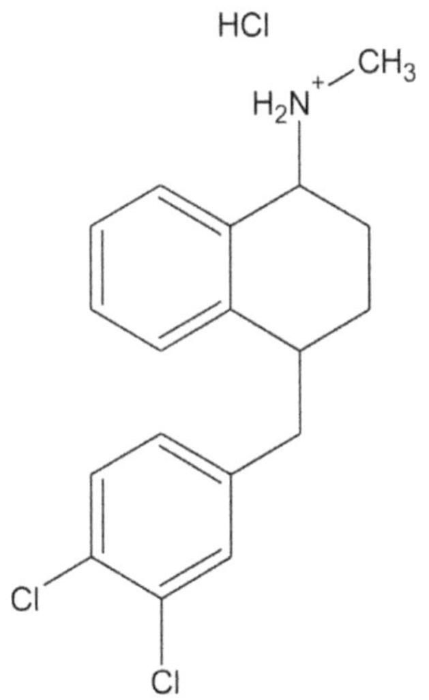

Sertraline

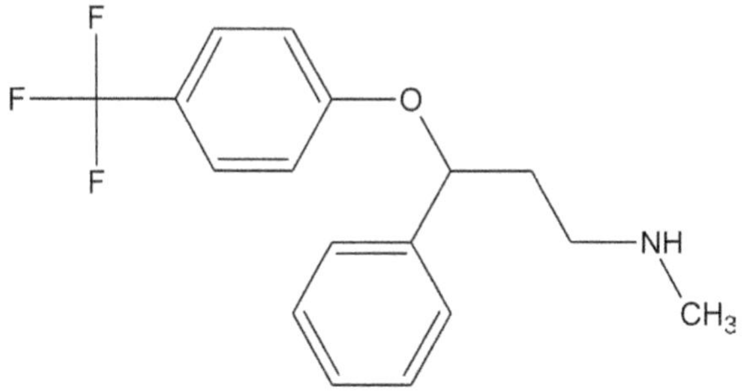

Fluoxetine

The first generation antidepressant drugs were called tricyclic anti-depressants and affected several neurotransmitters in the brain, particularly serotonin. Today there are a number of new antidepressants called serotonin-specific re-uptake inhibitors, SSRIs. Prozac was the first commercial SSRI. Zoloft is also a SSRI. Side-effects are varied but include insomnia, nausea, diarrhea, dry mouth, sexual dysfunction, and dizziness.

CANCER

Cancer is now the leading cause of death in the US. Cancer cells generally have three common characteristics. Cancer cells are not contact inhibited, that is, they will keep growing forming tumors rather than like normal cells that will grow until they touch another cell. Second, cancer cells are immortal. They will replicate 100s, 1,000s, and greater times. Most healthy cells replicate less than a dozen times in our lifetimes. Cancer cells will keep growing until they are killed. Third, cancer cells are essentially always in the growth mode whereas healthy cells are seldom in their growth mode. The cancer growth cycle is shown in Figure 14.2. We are developing drugs that will cause any of these steps to stop thereby inhibiting cancer cell growth. Most of the anticancer drugs act to inhibit cell growth by killing the cell as it metabolizes the anticancer drug during growth. Thus, if a healthy cell happens to be in a growth phase when chemo (the administration of anticancer drugs) is administered, that cell will likely be damaged or killed along with the target cancer cells. Of interest is that some cells that most often replicate themselves are found in the mouth and those resulting in hair growth. Thus, chemo often results in hair loss and a loss of taste.

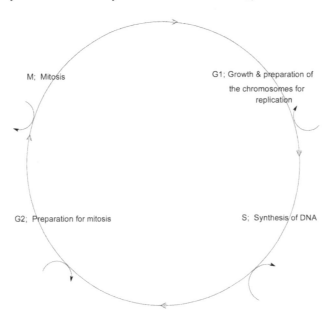

M; Mitosis

G1; Growth & preparation of the chromosomes for replication

G2; Preparation for mitosis

S; Synthesis of DNA

Figure 14.2 *Cell Growth Cycle*

Anticancer drugs include both synthetic drugs and natural drugs as taxol. Cis-diaminedichloroplatinum II, better known as **cisplatin**, is the most widely employed anticancer drug and it is a synthetic drug.

Cisplatin   Taxol

Taxol is a complex natural product isolated from the bark of the Pacific yew tree. Above is the approximate structure of taxol. By the late 1980s Holton's group at Florida State University developed a semi-synthetic synthesis of taxol allowing a ready supply of taxol and sparing the yew trees.

Structures for other chemo agents are given following. Most chemo agents are more active against only a few specific cancers. Thus, cisplatin is used against breast cancer and ovarian cancer. Its activity is believed to be related to its ability to bind certain bases on the DNA double helix thus preventing the DNA from replicating. **5-Flouorouracil** is mistaken by a cell for uracil. Because, while its structure is similar, its presence interferes with normal DNA activity resulting in the cell's death. Taxol and **vincristine** prevent the formation of cellular microstructures needed for cell division resulting in cell death.

Vincristine   5-Fluorouracil

Because cancer cells are in an almost constant growth mode they must have present high concentrations of certain biological nutrients such as dihydrofolic acid. **Methotrexate**, because of its structural similarity to **dihydrofolic acid**, binds to the receptor sites for dihydrofolic acid preventing these receptor sites from being active in the critical metabolic process thus inhibiting cell growth.

Dihydrofolic acid

Methotrexate

The unwanted side-effects for essentially all chemo drugs are horrific. Much research is being done to reduce the side-effects while retaining the anticancer activity.

HEART DISEASES

Heart-related diseases, namely heart attacks and strokes, are the second and third leading causes of death with cancer related deaths now number one. **"Heart attack"** is a broad grouping that directly involves the heart. **Strokes** generally involve the formation of a clot that prevents ready blood flow to the brain.

Arteriosclerosis is a buildup of plaque on the inside walls of arteries. (Why is plaque not built up on the outside?) Plaque-filled arteries are less flexible and have a smaller space to pump the blood so it takes more force to move the blood resulting in high blood pressure. This can lead to an abnormal heartbeat called **arrhythmia**. Chest pains, called **angina**, result from an insufficient oxygen supply to the heart.

Arteriosclerosis can also result in some plaque breaking off and clogging a blood vessel cutting off the blood supply. **Thrombosis** is a non-moving blood clot and an **embolism** is a moving blood clot. There are drugs that treat each of these symptoms.

High blood pressure or **hypertension** are terms employed to describe situations where additional pressure, supplied by the heart, is needed to maintain decent blood flow. Probably well over 50% of adults experience some sort of high blood pressure during their lifetime. There exists a variety of medical treatments including lowering weight, decreasing salt (mainly sodium chloride, table salt) intake, and increasing exercise.

Vasodilators are drugs that act to increase the blood supply to the heart through expanding blood vessels. Some individuals carry on their person vasodilators such as **nitroglycerin** and **amyl nitrite** tablets which when metabolized form nitric oxide, NO, which relaxes muscles in our blood vessels.

Of note, nitroglycerin is unstable because of the electron-withdrawing nature of the nitro groups. Another use of nitroglycerin is as an explosive. The nitroglycerine tablets are compounded to minimize this concern.

There are a number of other drugs available that treat hypertension at different junctures in the disease. Following are some of these general groupings.

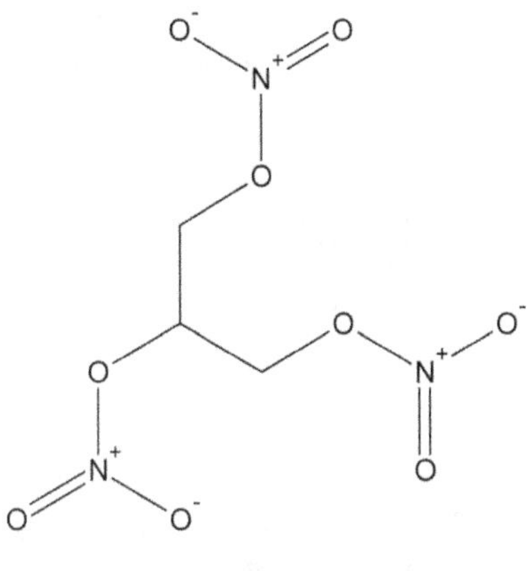

Nitroglycerin

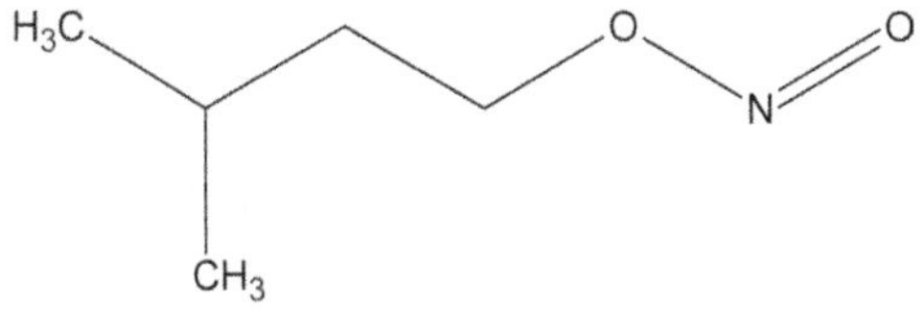

Amy nitrite

Beta blockers such as atenolol, labetalor, prepranolol (Inderal), and metoprolol (Lopressor, Toprol-XL) slow down and relax an overworked heart by blocking norepinephrine and epinephrine from binding to the beta-adrenoceptors. Both norephinephrine and epinephrine stimulate the heart to work faster and are generated when a person is in danger or excited. Many heart-related drugs do multiple duties. Along with treating high blood pressure, **prepranolol** is also employed to control arrhythmias and angina.

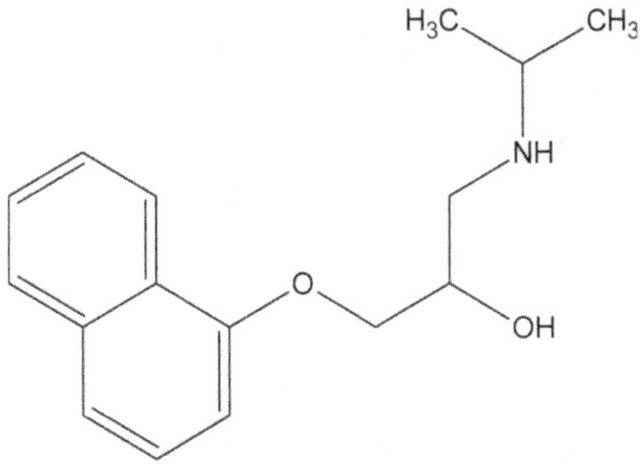

Prepranolol

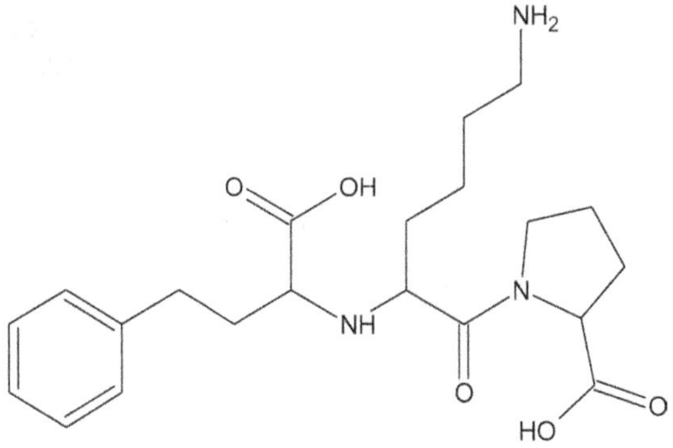

Lisinopril

ACE inhibitors such as **lisinopril** (Zestril), quinapril, captopril, enalapril, flosinopril (Monopril), and ramipril (Altace), act to decrease arteriolar resistance and increase venous capacity, heart output and volume.

Alpha Blockers, also called alpha-adrenergic blockers such as doxazosin, prazosin, and terazosin act to block alpha-adrenergic receptors in arteries and to smooth muscles intending to reduce the pressure needed to produce adequate blood flow.

Angiotensin II receptor antagonists such as telmisartan (Micardis, Pritor), **irbesartan** (Avapro), **valsartan** (Diovan), candesartan (Atacand), and losartan (Cozaar) are also known as angiotensin receptor blockers (ARBs), AT_1-receptor antagonists or sartans. They act to modulate the renin-angiotensin-aldosterone system. Their main use is in hypertension (high blood pressure), diabetic nephropathy (kidney damage due to diabetes) and congestive heart failure.

Valsartan (Diovan)   Irbesartan (Avapro)

Calcium channel blockers such as **nifedipine** (Adalat), diltiazem, vera-pamil, **amlodipine besylate**, and amlodipine (Norvasc) work by blocking the L-type voltage-gated calcium channels (VGCCs) in muscle cells of the heart and blood vessels preventing calcium levels from increasing as much in the cells when stimulated, leading to less muscle contraction. This acts to decrease in the heart the amount of calcium available for each beat resulting in a decreased cardiac contractility. In blood vessels, a decrease in calcium results in less contraction of the vascular smooth muscle and therefore an increase in blood vessel diameter, a phenomenon called vasodilation.

Nifedipine   Amlodiphine Besylate

Diuretics such as chloralidone, bendroflumethiazide, and **hydrochloro-thiazide** (HCTZ) act to lower the water content through increased urine production and sweating. There are a number of different diuretics that act differently and are effective for specific ailments. HCTZ reduces the sodium ion reabsorption in the distal convoluted tubule reducing the pressure in the kidney. In turn, this causes less water to be reabsorbed by the collecting duct resulting in increased urinary output.

Hydrochlorothiazide

ANTIBIOTICS

Bacteria are all about us with some being friendly helping us digest foods, others are being employed to make proteins from waste materials, still others are utilized to degrade and recycle materials. Bacteria are small (about 0.0003 to 0.002 millimeters; 0.00001 to 0.00008 inch) one-celled organisms occurring throughout our earth. A single cup of soil may contain more than 10,000,000,000 (10 billion) bacteria.

Most of the time bacteria do not cause diseases. They help in digestion and in destroying harmful microorganisms. Some intestinal bacteria produce needed vitamins. In the soil and water they assist in the recycling of nutrients. Many assist in the decay, decomposition of dead organisms and animal wastes. Some bacteria convert elemental nitrogen in the air, soil and water into nitrogen compounds needed by plants. Fermentation, used in making alcoholic beverages (converting sugar into ethanol ("drinking alcohol")), cheese and other foods, is caused by certain bacteria. Sewage treatment plants utilize bacteria to help in the purification of water. Bacteria are also employed in the synthesis of certain drugs.

Many of the harmful bacteria are harmful only when they are present in the "wrong" part of the body. A prime example of this is *E. coli* that is generally "harmless" but when found in the intestines cause food poisoning. Others such as anthrax are simply poison regardless to where they are in the body. Bacteria from the same family may exist in any number of strains that will exhibit the same general properties but which may demonstrate certain different properties. For instance, *Pseudomonas aeruginosa* strains can react towards selected drugs in a variety of ways depending on the particular strain. Unfortunately, strains found in hospitals are generally the most difficult to control and are called resistant strains. Some bacteria produce poisons, toxins which cause diseases such as tetanus, diphtheria and scarlet fever. Others produce toxins only after their demise. Some enter the body through sores, punctures, cuts and abrasions. Others are passed mistakenly from one organ to another. Bacteria also cause diseases in animals and plants.

Once in our body, harmful bacteria are met by white blood cells that attempt to kill them. Antibodies assist in the control of these invaders. When our body is not able to effectively control bacterial invasion, a physician may prescribe a shot and/or pills that contain an antitoxin from an animal or another person or a vaccine made from dead or weakened bacteria. The vaccines are injected to cause the body to increase its output of antibodies. Some vaccines protect the body for prolonged periods. Today antibiotics are usually the treatment of choice.

Bacteria are generally enclosed by a tough protective layer called a cell wall. The shape of the cell wall and its ability to retain or reject specified organic dyes (called stains) are used by scientists to identify the particular bacteria. There are four major "shapes of bacteria." Cocci are round and linked together. Bacilli are rod like, spirilla are spiral shaped, and vibrios appear as bent rods. Three prefixes can be added to these four major shapes to identify additional bacterial. Diplo is employed to describe paired shapes, strepto-chains and staphlo-clusters. Thus, a staphylococci is a cluster of round bacteria. The description of the size, shape, structure and arrangement of living objects is called the morphology of these living objects.

Many of the diseases are caused by bacteria. These include cholera, pneumonia, tuberculosis, and diphtheria. It is not known which biological organisms will be employed in an attempt to create bioterrorism but a number have been suggested. The first biological organism used in a biological attack was anthrax, a bacteria. Other bacteria, such as those responsible for typhoid, cholera, and the bubonic plague, have been suggested as possible candidates. Thus, developing materials that exhibit inhibition of a wide variety of bacteria is needed.

Drugs that act to inhibit bacteria are called **antibiotics**. These antibiotics act by inhibiting the reproduction of bacteria. Prior to the advent of antibiotics, bacterial infections were among the leading causes of death. Further, many bacteria evolve becoming resistant to often employed antibiotics. With the appearance of new resistant strains of common bacteria the need for new treatment rationales increases. The most insidious microorganism involved in nosocomial infections is methicillin-resistant *S. aureus*, MRSA (also called Staph MRSA). This microbe commonly colonizes those patients who are seriously ill and in high-risk areas such as intensive care and burn units. It is also a significant risk factor in surgical wound infections. The incident of MRSA infection in hospitals is increasing at an alarming rate. It can be carried in the anterior nares of otherwise healthy health-care givers and transferred to the patient during routine attendance at the patient's bedside. Other areas suspected of harboring the organism are air handling duct work, linens, and general room contamination. The incidences of MRSA infection occurring in the general population is increasing at a dangerous rate.

There are a number of categories of antibiotics. Historically, the penicillins are the most familiar to us. Penicillins were discovered by Fleming in 1928. Because of their limited activity, synthetic penicillins have been developed and almost exclusively employed today in place of the naturally grown penicillins.

Because of the importance of controlling the growth of unwanted bacteria a number of antibacterial agents have been developed.

With the recent anthrax scare, **ciprofloxacin** was the antibiotic of choice for those exposed to the anthrax. Because the anthrax was sent in the mail using a paper envelope all of the mail sites were tested for anthrax with many of them testing positive for the presence of anthrax. Had the anthrax been sent in a plastic envelop few if any of the sites would have tested positive. This illustrates the difference between paper and plastics such as polyethylene. The porosity of plastic envelops is much less than that of paper.

While both are polymeric, polyethylene chains form a close web of chains such than only gas molecules can easily penetrate. By comparison, paper is composed of cellulose bundles that can be seen by holding a piece of paper up to the light. These bundles have a much greater space between them that allow anthrax spores to penetrate the envelope thus contaminating areas surrounding the anthrax-containing envelope.

Examples of antibiotics include

cephalosporins- cephalexin (keflex), cefaclor (ceclor), cefixime (suprax), cefeime (masiprime)
glycopeptides- vancomycin (vancocin), clarithromycin (biaxin)
penicillins- amoxicillin, **ampicillin, tricarcillin**, nafcillin
quinolones- ciprofloxacin (cipro, ciproxin), levofloxacin (levaguin), **norfloxacin**, lomefloxacin
sulfonamides - sulfamethizole, **trimethoprim**, trimethoprim-sulfamethoxazole (bactrim)
tetracyclines- dexcycline (vibramycin), minocycline (minocin), **tetracycline** (sumycin)

The structure of some of the best known antibiotics is given below.

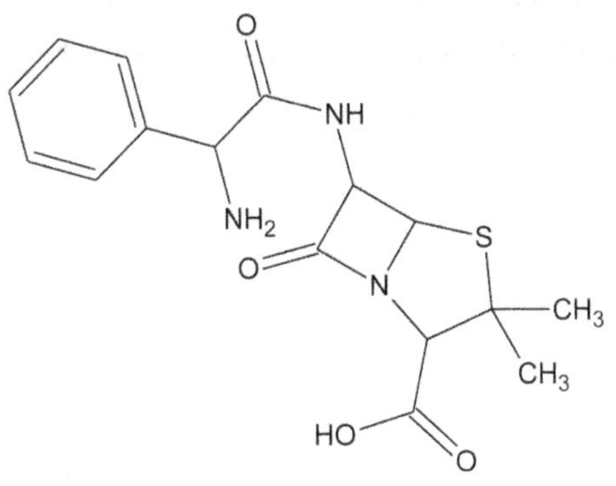

Ampicillin

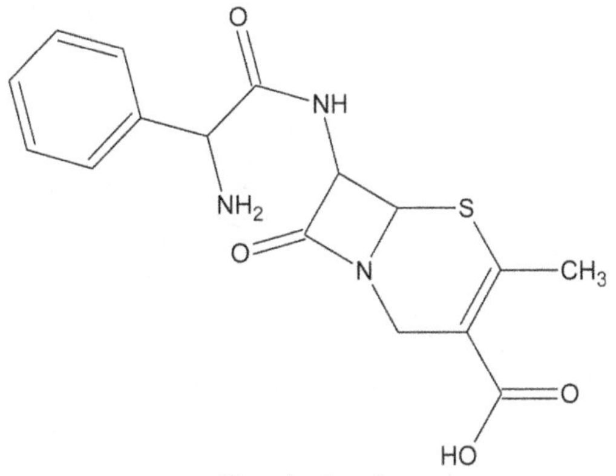

Cephalexin

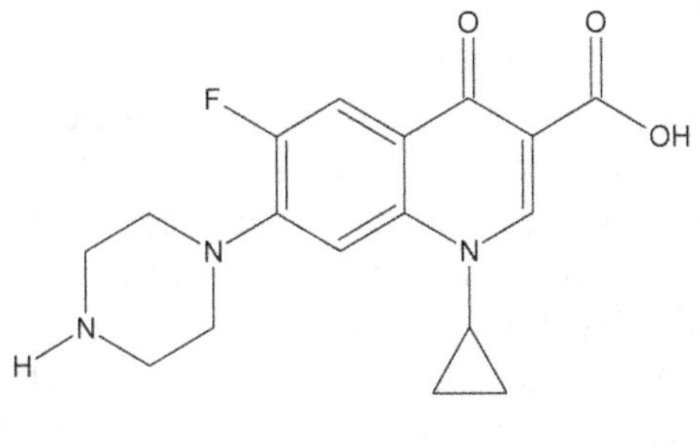

Ciprofloxacin

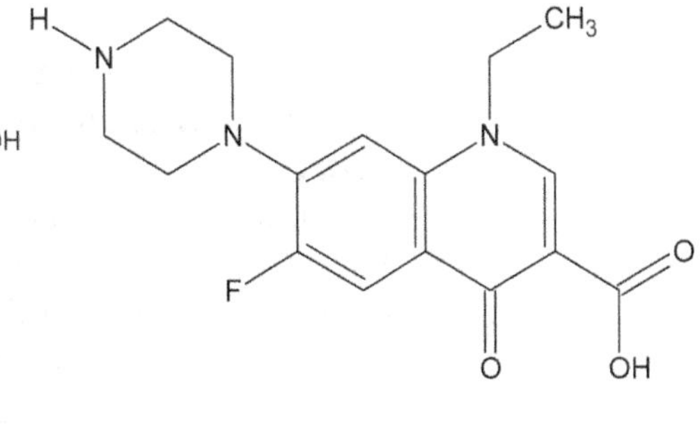

Norfloxacin

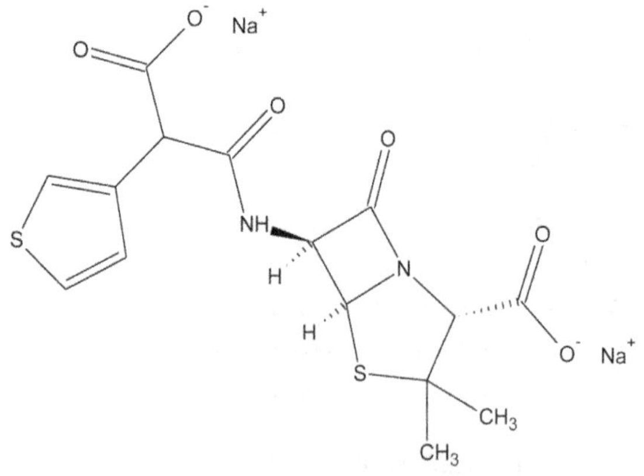

Ticarcillin

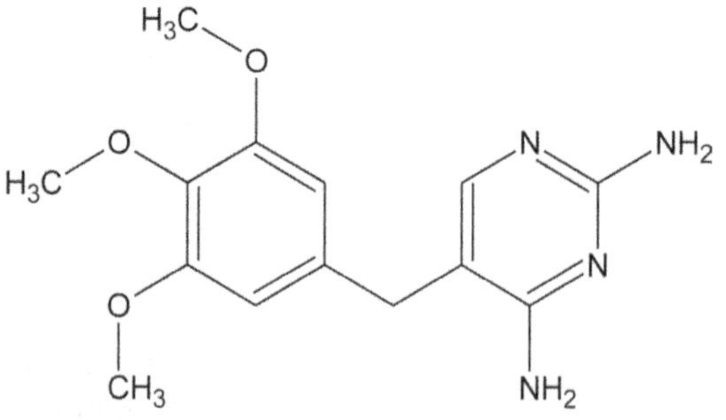

Trimethoprim

Another group of antibiotics are composed of a group of compounds that contain four fused-rings called tetracyclines. These drugs bind bacterial ribosomes inhibiting protein synthesis resulting in bacterial death. Included in this group are **tetracycline** itself, aureomycin, and **terramycin**.

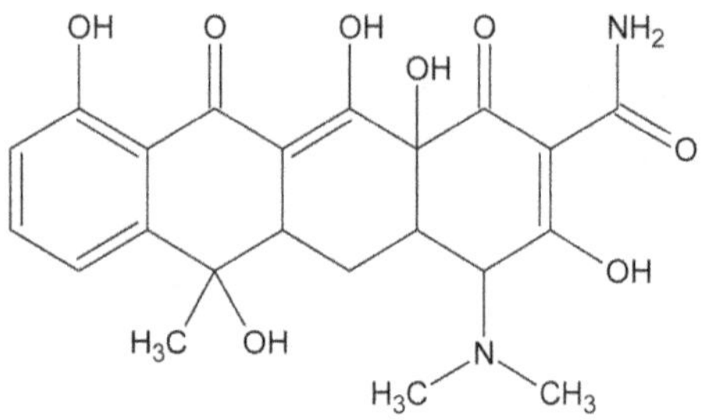

Tetracycline

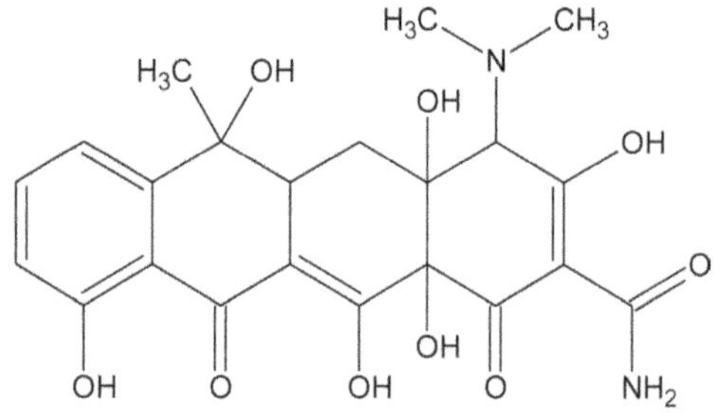

Terramycin

Sulfa drugs have been used since the 1930s to treat specific bacterial infections. They are structurally similar to **para-aminobenzoic acid,** PABA, at one time a common ingredient in sun screen lotions. PABA works taking advantage of a difference between humans and bacteria. Both humans and bacteria need folic acid. Humans obtain it from what we eat. Bacteria, by comparison, must synthesize it. For this, bacteria possess enzymes that help make **folic acid** from PABA. Because sulfa drugs are structurally similar to PABA the sulfa drugs get inserted in place of PABA occupying the site on the enzyme. This prohibits PABA from entering into the synthetic process thus eventually killing the bacteria since it cannot obtain the essential folic acid. One sulfa drug, **sulfanilamide,** is shown below as is folic acid. Note the center structure of folic acid is the one where PABA is needed.

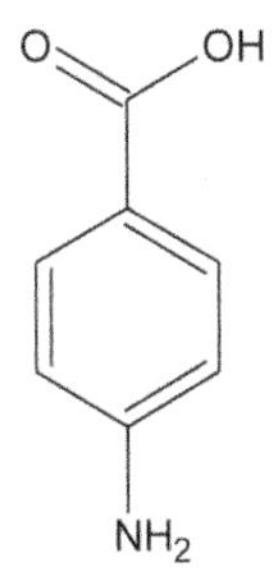

PABA

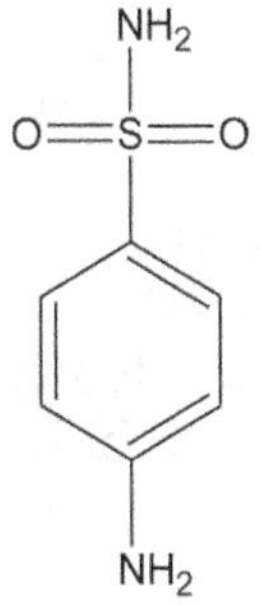

Sulfanilamide

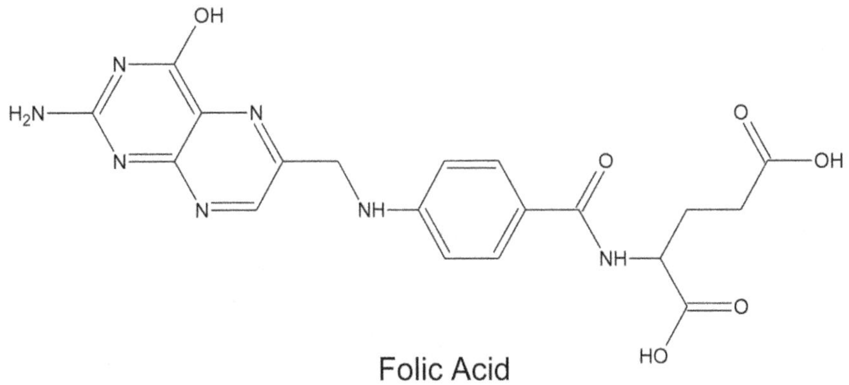

Folic Acid

VIRUSES

In contrast to bacteria that are single-celled living organisms that replicate on their own, viruses require the machinery of a host cell to replicate. Most viruses consist of only some protein and DNA. The virus infects a cell high-jacking the cells reproductive system for their own use. The newly reproduced viruses infect other cells, until there is a full blown viral infection. Antibiotics are not effective at fighting viruses. Viral attacks are common and are responsible for what we call the common cold as well as flu, polio, measles, chicken pox, herpes, and the acquired immune deficiency syndrome (AIDS). Unlike most viruses the AIDS virus contains RNA and protein with the RNA reversing its usual role creating DNA from its template. This reverse transcription to create its own DNA allows the virus to produce its own viral protein from the newly formed DNA.

Until the early 1970s there were no effective synthetic antiviral agents. The first of the synthetic antiviral agents, acyclovir, was developed by Welcome labs in 1974. **Acyclovir** is a synthetic purine nucleoside that exhibits *in vitro* and *in vivo* inhibition of a number of human viruses. In particular, acyclovir is active against herpes simplex types 1 (HSV-1) and 2 (HSV-2) viruses, varicella-zoster virus (VZV), Epstein-Barr virus (EBV), and cytomegalovirus (CMV). The inhibitory activity of acyclovir is highly selective. The enzyme thymidine kinase of normal cells does not effectively use acyclovir but thymidine kinase, encoded by one of the viruses noted above, converts acyclovir into acyclovir monophosphate and this is converted into the diphosphate by cellular guanylate kinase; and finally, it is converted by a number of enzymes into the triphosphate. The triphosphate interferes with herpes simplex virus DNA polymerase and inhibits viral DNA replication. The acyclovir is then less toxic to normal cells because less is taken up, less is converted to the active form, and cellular alpha-DNA polymerase is less sensitive to the active form. Acyclovir is a member of a group of antiviral agents considered nucleoside analogs.

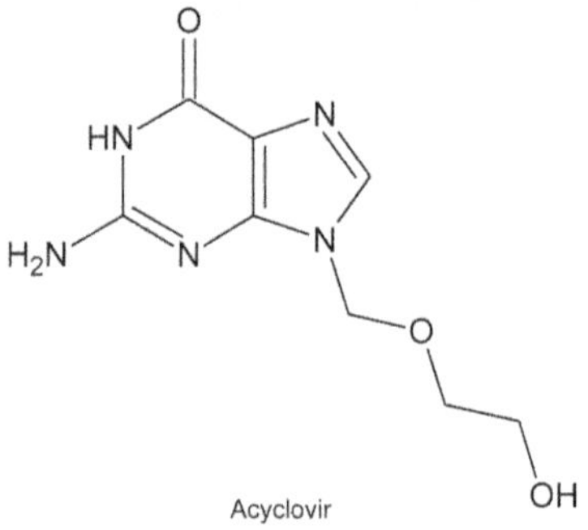

Acyclovir

Since the advent of acyclovir other antiviral agents have been synthesized. One group of antiviral agents focuses on the inhibition of certain protein enzymes and is referred to as protease inhibitors. **Indinavir** and ritonavir are two members of this group that are mainly utilized to combat the HIV virus. In 1989 researchers determined the three-dimensional structure of the HIV enzyme. It looked like a butterfly with two wings. By the early 1990s a number of butterfly-like structures were investigated. Several drugs were successful in occupying the butterfly-site preventing the active site to function. This resulted in curtailing protein growth and subsequent reproduction of the virus. Note the butterfly-like structure of indinavir.

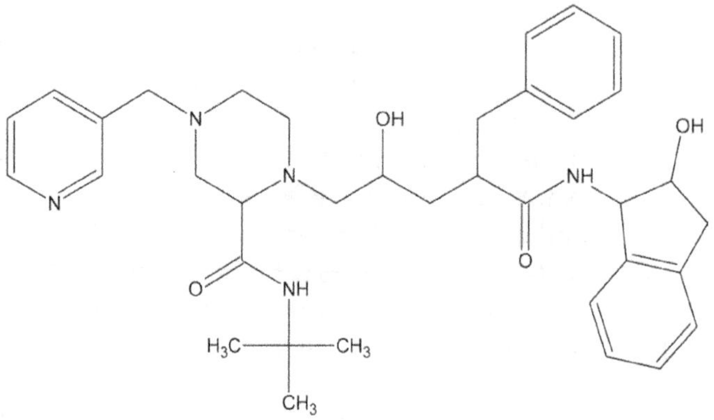

Indinavir

STEROIDS

Steroids are a group of lipids. They contain a general structure consisting of four fused rings. Many of the steroids are hormones that are produced by one part of the body to affect other parts of the body. Cholesterol is the most common, by weight, steroid composing about 10% of our brains weight. It is synthesized in the liver though we also get it from eating especially meat.

Many steroidal hormones are related to which sex we are. Men continually produce **testosterone** while women produce estrogen (**estradiol** and **estrone**) and **progesterone** in the ovaries in a cyclic manner. Early birth control pills were synthetic sex hormones. Estrogen-like drugs gave the body a false sense that it was pregnant thus preventing the release of eggs.

General Steroidal Structure   Testosterone

Estradiol   Estrone   Progesterone

Adrenocortical steroids such as **prednisone** and **cortisone** are normally taken as anti-inflammatory drugs. Swelling is part of our body's normal defense system. When a part of our body is damaged or invaded by an unwanted object, blood proteins and other materials are transported to the damaged area resulting in swelling. Adrenocortical steroids work by suppressing our inflammatory and immune responses to these repeated stresses (so-called tennis elbow) and the presence of foreign or unwanted objects (such as bone chips, splinters). The steroids can be directly injected to the site or taken by pill. While adrenocortical steroid use helps reduce inflammation it can result in unwanted side-effects such as liquid retention, loss of bone mass, suppression of our immune system, increased weight gain, etc.

Prednisone   Cortisone

Anabolic steroids have often been used by athletics to gain muscle since they increase protein synthesis. Today, we know that their extended use is dangerous resulting in males a loss in sperm production and testicular atrophy. In females it causes the user to assume male characteristics, since most anabolic steroids are synthetic versions of the male testosterone hormone. In both sexes it increases the risk of heart attacks and strokes. Their use is illegal. These anabolic steroids go under a variety of names including **stanazolol** (Winstrol, Winstrol Depot) and **boldenone** (Equipoise, Ultragan, Equigan, Ganabol).

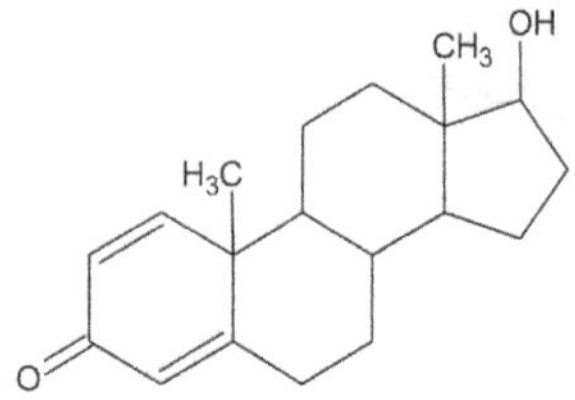

Boldenone

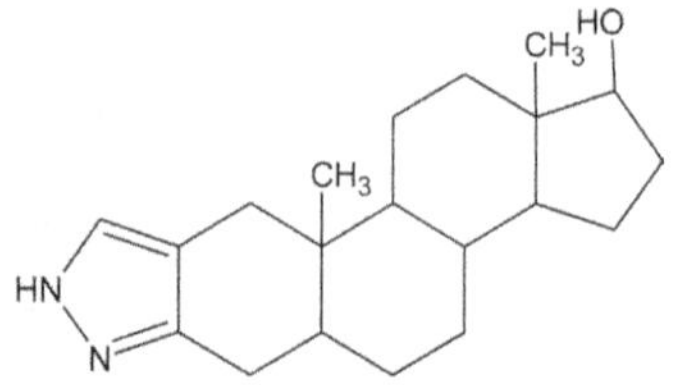

Stanozolol

Food

As we do, plants also require nutrients -minerals and organic building blocks. Plants produce their major building block, carbohydrates or saccharides, through **photosynthesis**- the conversion of carbon dioxide and water, with the help of sunlight and chlorophyll to produce sugars, etc. Thus, the ultimate source for most food production is the sun and photosynthesis.

$$CO_2 + H_2O \longrightarrow carbohydrate + O_2$$

Porphyrin   Heme

Porphyrin (left) structures serve as the basis of **heme** (right) in animals. Upon addition of iron, this porphyrin, which is called protoporphyrin IX, forms the heme group (right) assisting in the transport of oxygen through our blood.

Chlorophyll

Plants use a similar structure, **chlorophyll**, as a basis for photosynthesis. Chlorophyll is green colored, hence the green in plant leaves.

To fix nitrogen is to put it in a form (compound) that is useful to plants. Many plants are unable to fix nitrogen and must depend on external sources for their nitrogen. Lightening is sufficiently strong to break the nitrogen triple bonds allowing formation of various nitrogen oxides (source of acid rain) and other nitrogen-containing compounds. Thus, much nitrogen is fixed by lightning.

$$N_2 + 3O_2 + 2e^{-1} \rightarrow 2NO_3^{-1}$$

Synthetic fertilizers are one source of nitrogen for plants. Probably the most widely used process making usable nitrogen is the **Haber process** which uses nitrogen and hydrogen from the air to make ammonia.

$$N_2 + 3H_2 \leftrightarrows 2NH_3$$

Soil is composed of inorganics, often salts including minerals and silicates (sand, silicon dioxide) and organics- degraded plant and animal material. Soil is also a means to purify water. The Florida Everglades is a major ecotourism site. It also supplies much of the drinking water for south Florida. Flow of water through soil is called **percolation** and removal of material is **leaching**. Depending on the particular minerals, inorganics, the soil can have a high (basic) or low (acidic) pH. Carbon dioxide often determines the soil pH. Carbon dioxide acts like it forms carbonic acid, which is a weak acid. The more carbon dioxide, the lower the pH, normally not below a pH of 5, so it is not too acidic.

$$H_2O + CO_2 \rightarrow H_2CO_3 \leftrightarrows H^{+1} + HCO_3^{-1}$$

As noted, fertilizers are often used to deliver needed nutrients. A mixed or complete fertilizer often contains nitrogen-phosphorus-potassium and may be a combination of NH_4NO_3 and some phosphorus oxide like P_2O_5 (which is really P_4O_{10}), and a source of potassium such as KNO_3 or K_2O (potash) in some ratio giving something like a 12-24-12 which is 12% N-24%P-12%K.

PESTICIDES

For every good there may well be a bad. Often there are unintended consequences. How do these statements pertain to pesticides? Some chemicals accumulate in certain species, **bioaccumulation**, so that a "not bad" general concentration now becomes a bad concentration. Chlorinated hydrocarbons are one group-**BCBs**, polychlorinated biphenyls, of materials that bioaccumulates. The half-life in fish is long so it accumulates in them and when we fish depending on what the fish has eaten, we may get too much of the unwanted chemical.

PCB

DDT

DDT is another material that is good for killing unwanted bugs allowing the growth of essential food. But it has been found to accumulate in birds causing their eggs to be so thin that the birds are not able to hatch them, sit on them, without breaking them. DDT was outlawed for this reason in the US but it is still widely used in third world countries where it kills bugs that would otherwise devour the food necessary for the inhabitants to survive. Thus, there is a tension between birds and people.

If a chemical is supposed to kill one species- bacterial, bacteria, virus, weeds, pests, it is logical that it is not good, in some concentration, for us. What are questions we should ask when investigating such agents? Can weeds play a positive role in erosion control? Is so-called organic grown food better? Why/why not? Today the official definition of organically grown may not be what you think it is. One thing to remember is that it generally takes more fertilizer and plant care to raise organically grown food.

Potential pesticides are generally now tested on animals before they are sold commercially. What are alternatives to animal testing? What happens to it and when (time frame) after it is applied in the field? What is the cost/benefit for this agent? How toxic is it? Are elderly, children and pregnant mothers more susceptible? What are acceptable answers?

Alternatives to the use of pesticides include pheromones, application of technology, gene or transgenic seeds (plants) (risks?). It is said that our food problem is not one of supply but rather one of location. What does this mean and can it really be solved?

Fresh Water

Most of Earth's water has salt in it- saline water. Much of the remaining is frozen. The major source of water is the ocean and the major source of fresh water is the polar caps. Water runs through a "hydrologic cycle." We have surface (lakes, oceans, rivers), ground (in the ground), and atmospheric water. In south Florida we get about 3 million acre feet yearly- one million acre foot is moved from back to the clouds by evaporation, one million acre foot into the canals and used by us for lawns and drinking; and one million acre foot becomes ground water. We can capture some of this and hold it for a "rainy day" or "not so rainy day."

The hydrologic cycle is rain (precipitation) → surface, runoff, ground, use → evaporation → rain → Etc.

The water aquifer includes both surface and ground water that is being held by the soil or beneath the soil. The water table is the saturated ground level with the depth of the water table variable depending on what is beneath it. While we consume lots of water, we do not consume as much as is often indicated. And, much of this is needed consumption in our societal framework. Stick a brick in our toilet closet. Does this really save water and if so how much? If we recycle water it comes at a cost. What is the cost? What are the pros/cons to our water treatment as it is practiced today? Introduction of (sometimes) unwanted chemicals to give us clean and safe water-fluorination, chlorination and microbes- how safe is this?

Our Atmosphere

Our atmosphere is shared-we get and give to Canada acid rain; from Europe we get lots of mercury and other pollutants.

We have some real concerns including global warming and the depletion of the ozone layer. The atmosphere is not very dense and it becomes less dense as we travel away from the earth. The ozone layer resides within the stratosphere. It takes about 50 years for most things to go from ground level to the altitude of the ozone layer about 20-30 kilometers or about 10–15 miles. The ozone layer helps protect us from harmful UV radiation- that has sufficient energy to break bonds and cause skin cancer.

Smog. Industrial smog is formed from the combustion of coal and petrochemicals that gives sulfur and nitrogen oxides that then become weak to strong acids giving us acid rain. Photochemical smog is caused by pollutants that take part in chemical reactions induced by sunlight. Some of the compounds are good and some are bad.

The **greenhouse effect** is a global warming problem. The earth is at some kind of equilibrium that needs to be maintained or there are unintended consequences with one thing influencing another, etc. As we burn the fossil fuels we create needed energy, unwanted nitrogen and sulfur oxides (acid rain), and unwanted particulates (greenhouse effect). What occurs is that sunlight comes into our atmosphere and then, rather than bouncing back away from our atmosphere, it is bounced by the particulates back to the earth with another chance to give up its energy thus creating additional warmth. As with most problems we need to judge the consequences of "missing" the solution. If those consequences may be the end to civilization as we know it, then it is better to error on the side of caution and to act as though it may occur and act in a reasonable manner to prevent it.

Material Sources

Our sources are at once both many and limited. Renewable resources include trees, plants so polysaccharides (cotton and starch), rubber, lignin.

Many of the reactants used for the production of polymers are standard organic chemicals. However, because of the high purity requirements and large amounts needed, special conditions have been developed that allow large amounts of high purity reactants to be made in high yield.

Most of the monomers widely employed for both vinyl and condensation polymers are derived indirectly from simple feedstock molecules. This synthesis of monomers is a lesson in inventiveness. The application of the saying that "necessity is the mother of invention" has led to the sequence of chemical reactions where little is wasted and byproducts from one reaction are employed as integral materials in another. It must be remembered that often many years of effort were involved in discovering the conditions of pressure, temperature, catalysts, etc., that must be present as one goes from the starting materials to the products.

Further, there is a giant move towards green science. Thus, many of the monomers, and other materials made by us, are being made using renewable sources as the feedstocks.

FOSSIL FUELS

Fossil fuels refer to materials formed from the decomposition of once living matter. Because these once living materials contain sulfur and heavy metals such as iron and cobalt, they must be removed either prior or subsequent to use.

The major fossil fuels are coal and petroleum. Marine organisms were typically deposited in muds and under water, where anaerobic decay occurred. The major decomposition products are hydrocarbons, carbon dioxide, water, and ammonium. These deposits form much of the basis for our petroleum resources. Many of these deposits are situated so that the evaporation of the more volatile products such as water and ammonia occurred, giving petroleum resources with little nitrogen- or oxygen-containing products. By comparison, coal is formed from plant material that has decayed to graphite carbon and methane.

Only about 5% of the fossil fuels consumed today are used as feedstocks for the production of today's synthetic carbon-based products. This includes the products produced by the chemical and drug industries with a major portion acting as the feedstocks for plastics, elastomers, coatings, fibers, etc.

The major petroleum resources contain linear, saturated hydrocarbons (alkanes), cyclic alkanes, and aromatics. Raw or crude petroleum materials are separated into groups of compounds with similar boiling points by a process called **fractionation**. Accompanying or subsequent to fractionation occurs a process called "**cracking**" whereby the hydrocarbon molecules are heated over catalysts that allow the hydrocarbon molecules to break up and then reform into structures that contain more branching that allow for good combustion in our automobiles and trucks. Under other conditions, the cracking allows the formation of other desired feedstock molecules including methane, ethane, ethylene, propylene, benzene, etc. that eventually become our plastics, fibers, elastomers, sealants, coatings, composites, etc.

PAPER

It is believed that paper was invented by Ts'ai in China around the second century AD. The original paper was a mixture of bark and hemp. Paper was first produced in the US by William Rittenhouse in Germantown, PA in 1690 and this paper was made from rags. Paper was named after the papyrus plant, *Cyperus papyrus*.

Paper comes in many forms with many uses. The book you are reading is made from paper, we have paper plates, paper napkins, newspapers and magazines, cardboard boxes, in fact the amount of paper items is probably over twice, by weight, that of all the synthetic polymers combined. About 30 % paper is writing and printing paper. The rest is mainly used for tissues, toweling, and packaging. If you rip a piece of ordinary paper, not your book page please, you will see that it consists of small fibers. Most of these cellulosic fibers are randomly oriented, but a small percentage is oriented in one direction because the paper is made from a cellulose-derived watery slurry with the water largely removed through use of heated rollers.

Modern paper is made from wood pulp, largely cellulose, which is obtained by the removal of lignin from debarked wood chips by use of chemical treatments with sodium hydroxide, sodium sulfite, or sodium sulfate. Newsprint and paperboard, which is thicker than paper, often contains a greater amount of residual lignin.

Wood is almost entirely composed of cellulose and lignin. In the simplest paper making scheme, the wood is chopped, actually torn, into smaller fibrous particles as it is pressed against a rapidly moving pulpstone. A stream of water washes the fibers away dissolving much of the water-soluble lignin. The insoluble cellulosic fibers are concentrated into a paste called **pulp**. The pulp is layered into thin sheets and rollers are used to both squeeze out much of the water and to assist in achieving paper of uniform thickness. This paper is not very white. It is also not very strong because the remaining lignin is somewhat acidic (lignin contains acidic phenolic groups that hydrolyze to give a weakly acidic aqueous solution) that causes the hydrolytic breakdown of the cellulose. Most of the newsprint is of this type or it is regenerated reused paper.

Pulping processes are designed to remove the non-saccharide lignin portion of wood which constitutes about 25 of the dry weight. The remaining is mostly cellulose with about 25 % hemicellulose (noncellulose cell wall polysaccharides that are easily extracted by dilute aqueous base solutions). Pulping procedures can be generally classified as semichemical, chemical, and semimechanical. In semimechanical pulping, the wood is treated with water or sulfate, bisulfite, or bicarbonate solution that softens the lignin. The pulp is then ground or shredded to remove much of the lignin giving a purified or enriched cellulose content. The semichemical process is similar but digestion times are longer and digesting solutions more concentrated giving a product with less lignin but the overall yield of cellulose-intense material is lowered by 70 to 80 %. Further, some degradation of the cellulose occurs.

Most paper is produced by the chemical process where chemicals are employed to solubilize and remove most of the lignin. While overall yields are lower than the other two main processes, the product gives good quality writing and printing paper. Three main chemical processes are used. In the soda process extracting solutions containing about 25% sodium hydroxide and 2.4 % sodium carbonate are used. In the sulfite process the extracting solution contains a mixture of calcium dihydrogen sulfite and sulfur dioxide. The sulfide process utilizes sodium hydroxide, sodium monosulfide, and sodium carbonate in the extracting solution.

After the chemical treatment, the pulped wood is removed, washed, and screened. Unbleached, brown-colored paper is made directly for this material. Most whiten or bleached paper is made from treatment of the pulp with chlorine, chlorine dioxide, hypochlorite, and/or alkaline extraction. In general, sulfate pulped paper is darker and requires more bleaching and alkaline extraction to give a "white" pulp.

The sulfide process, also called the kraft process (the term "kraft" comes from the Swedish word for strong since stronger paper is produced), is more commonly used. The kraft process is favored over the sulfite treatment of the paper because of environmental considerations. The sulfite process employs more chemicals that must be disposed of-particularly mercaptans, RSHs that are quite odorous. Research continues on reclaiming and recycling pulping chemicals.

If pure cellulose was solely used to make paper, the fiber mat would be somewhat water soluble with only particle surface polar groups and internal hydrogen bonding acting to hold the fibers together. White pigments such as clay and titanium dioxide are added to help "cement" the fibers together and to fill voids producing a firm, white writing surface. This often occurs as part of an overall coating process.

Most paper is coated to provide added strength and smoothness. The coating is basically an inexpensive paint that contains a pigment and a small amount of polymeric binder. Unlike most painted surfaces, most paper products are manufactured with a short life time in mind with moderate performance requirements. Typical pigments are inexpensive low-refractive index materials such as plate-like clay and ground natural calcium carbonate. Titanium dioxide is used only when high opacity is required. The binder may be a starch or latex or a combination of these. The latexes are usually copolymers of styrene, butadiene, acrylic, and vinyl acetate. Other additives and coloring agents may also be added for special performance papers. Resins, in the form of surface coating agents and other special surface treatments (such as coating with polypropylene and polyethylene), are used for paper products intended for special uses such as milk cartons, ice cream cartons, light building materials, and drinking cups. The cellulose supplies the majority of the weight (typically about 90 %) and strength with the special additives and coatings providing special properties needed for the intended use.

Recycling of paper continues to good advantage. Today, up to about one half of our paper products are recycled and this fraction is increasing as we do a better job of collecting and recycling paper products.

Energy Sources

Electricity is the most widely used energy source-but it must be generated and it is largely generated from the combustion (burning) of coal (30%) and petroleum (38% oil and 20% natural gas- methane largely; total 58%) products.

There are lots of units of power (rate at which electrical energy or other form of energy is used up). One unit of power is watt

$$1 \text{ watt} = 1 \text{ joule}/1 \text{ second or J/s}$$

Our electric bills often have our cost based on kilowatt-hours, that is the amount of energy consumed in one hour. A kilowatt is 1000 joules/second. At home we may use the units of kw-hours. How would you convert J/s to kw?

Let us calculate the energy of using one 100 watt bulb for 2 hours and what would be its cost if 1 killowatt hour costs 20 cents (or 0.20 dollar)

100 watts is 0.1 kw; For two hours this is 0.1 kw $\times$ 2 hours or 0.2 kw-hours. The cost is 0.2 kw-hours $\times$ 0.2 dollars/kw-hour = 0.4 dollars or 40 cents.

It took many years to create the fossil fuels (petroleum and coal; why are they called fossil fuels) and we are using them up fast. Also, petroleum forms the basis for most of the polymers and medicines we use today-about 5%. There are different amounts of contaminants in these fossil fuels depending on where they are from.

We also get about 10–20% of our energy from nuclear fission but nuclear fusion is being looked at as the energy source of the future- essentially no lasting bad byproducts. What are potential pros/cons for nuclear fission? Why do we use radioactive uranium as our fuel?

Alternative sources- hydroelectric from flowing water, ocean tidal energy, hydrothermal from volcano or hot surface, wind, burning waste (lignin- problem), other biomass (conversion of corn cobs to automotive fuels), solar energy converters, conservation (smart windows).

ENERGY SOURCES

The more typical forms of energy include natural gas (mostly methane), coal, petrochemical, and nuclear. There are a number of "new" or alternative energy sources that are being considered and their use is increasing. Currently, each has some problems before they can supply a major fraction of our energy needs. But, combined they can supply a major part of our future energy needs. More can be known about each of these topics, and other newer based alternative energy sources by looking at the web.

Hydrogen fusion- a copy of what the sun does. While we have run a hydrogen fusion reaction, it has not been sustained for more than fractions of a second and has taken more energy than it generated. Eventually, this is our long range energy solution but it will be decades before it comes on line, thus we need to look at potential short term solutions.

Wind- a wind turbine costs from $250,000 to $1 million to construct and wind is not constant. Thus it will need to be part of an energy grid. A decent generator can supply energy for about 300 homes. Www.awea.org

Solar- photovoltaics cost about $14,000 to 20,000 for a decent home system but again, it will need to be part of a home's energy network. The "mirror on the roof" is now outdated though they are still sold. Technology with photovoltaics has out run these systems. Solartoday.org is a magazine that tells about solar energy.

Ethanol- while ethanol today is primarily obtained from corn, the sources will need to be enlarged. Many places are now selling a 10% ethanol/90% petro mix known as E10. Ethanol, compared to gasoline, burns at a higher temperature and gives less energy resulting in lowered mpg. It also requires energy to produce resulting in a created energy of near 60% compared with gasoline that gives near a 95% net energy creation. Brazil is trying to go totally to ethanol as a fuel and they are working on enlarging the market. Automobiles will need to be modified to take a largely ethanol fuel from modifying the motors to new gaskets. Look at E85Fuel.com for more information. Ethanol production generally comes from corn so is competing with a needed food. Fortunately, we can make ethanol and methanol from bacteria that utilize leaves, corn-stalks, etc. as feedstocks.

Biodiesel- is made from crops such as soybeans. It is being promoted as reducing emissions. Diesels can today run on biodiesel with little or no modification. Again, as is the case with ethanol, biodiesel takes energy to produce so that must be part of the consideration. Today, biodiesel costs about the same as regular diesel. For more information go to Biodiesel.org.

Nuclear- there is proposed new plants to be constructed to produce energy. Today, about 20% of our energy is nuclear. The infrastructure is already present to allow us to bring more plants on line. The negatives are potential nuclear disasters, having to get rid of "spend" uranium, and the cost of the plant. For more information go to World-Nuclear.org.

Hydrogen- there is lots of research being done related to a hydrogen fuel economy. Currently, there are lots of problems including distribution, safety, and cost of production. Hydrogen gas plus oxygen react giving water and lots of energy. Hydrogen containment is a major problem. Carbon nanotubes are being considered as holders of hydrogen. Hydrogen is generally considered being formed from the electrodialysis of water- the reverse reaction of hydrogen gas and oxygen gas forming water and energy. Thus, energy must be supplied to create the hydrogen and oxygen.

Battery- again lots of research is being done to develop batteries that operate longer, cost less, weight less, and that are more efficient. Today, hybrid and totally battery operated cars are available. These cars have limited ranges though progress is occurring. It is important to note that the batteries must be recharged either through electrical connection which simply shifts the location of energy creation or by it recharging itself (a better solution). Technology is developing and promising.

Wave production- wave production using not only waves to drive tiny turbines but uses tidal and natural underwater currents to drive turbines that create energy either directly or through creation of hydrogen is being studied. The ability to do this has already been shown so it is a matter of doing so in a larger and more economically feasible manner.

Dams- Hydro electronic plants have been in operation for many years and others are being added. These are generally clean but it takes years for the cost to be recovered.

Geothermal- again, there are various forms being studied and some used. One plan involves creating a piping system about a home where the pipes extend into the ground to capture coolness during the summer and heat during the winter.

CPSIA information can be obtained
at www.ICGtesting.com
Printed in the USA
BVHW062158290622
640986BV00004B/31